THE CANONGATE PRIZE
FOR NEW WRITING

*Scotland into the
New Era*

THE CANONGATE PRIZE
FOR NEW WRITING

Scotland into the New Era

Canongate Books
IN ASSOCIATION WITH

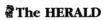

The HERALD · W · sundayherald

WATERSTONE'S

First published in Great Britain in 2000 by
Canongate Books Ltd, 14 High Street,
Edinburgh EH1 1TE

10 9 8 7 6 5 4 3 2 1

The publishers acknowledge subsidy from the
Scottish Arts Council towards the publication
of this volume

**For further information about the Canongate Prize for
New Writing, and details of how to enter next year's
competition, please contact:
www.canongateprize.com**

British Library Cataloguing-in-Publication Data
A catalogue record for this book is available
on request from the British Library

ISBN 0 86241 935 2

Typeset by Hewer Text Ltd, Edinburgh
Printed and bound by Caledonian International Book
Manufacturing, Bishopbriggs, Glasgow

Contents

Foreword

When I was approached, in December 1998, by Aly Burt, Andrew Johnson and Iain MacFarlane from Waterstone's, with the notion of starting a new prize for writing, I had no idea that in just over a year we would have successfully launched the inaugural competition and published the first book of winning entries. But here, in your hands, is that book.

The vision from the outset was to start a competition that was unlike any other. Certain things made it particularly distinct: first that all forms of prose would be eligible; secondly that there would be no single winner but a group of winners, all of whom would receive the same prize; thirdly that we would set a theme that would change each year; and finally that each piece would be read initially by at least four different people from a pool of sixty Waterstone's employees.

Teaming up with Waterstone's, *The Herald* and *Sunday Herald*, provided an ideal group of like-minded partners, allowing us to kick-start the prize in a way that resulted in a massive range of entries – 1,251 in this first year.

I cannot discuss each of the winning seventeen entries in detail here but feel that each of them offers something original that engages with the theme. Of course I have favourites, as did the other six people who sat on the judging panel, but it is the diversity of the entries that excited me, some written by established authors, others by people for whom this will be their first published piece.

The panel for the first year was made up of myself, Judy Moir (senior editor at Canongate), Kate Atkinson (the award-winning novelist), Alex Linklater (literary editor of *The Herald*), Pat Kane (arts editor of the *Sunday Herald*), Gordon Kerr (marketing director of Waterstone's) and Peter Kravitz (broadcaster, editor and journalist). The task of selecting the winning entries with this group of people was a fascinating and hugely enjoyable one as we sat round a table, discussing each anonymous piece in turn.

One piece does need to be mentioned as for legal reasons we felt it too risky to include it in this anthology despite it being selected as one of the original seventeen winners. Peter Dorward wrote an outstanding and deeply chilling story entitled 'Wullie Unbound', that took the fictional cartoon character Oor Wullie and explored in a highly imaginative way what happened to this boy in later life. Sadly the *Sunday Post* made it clear that they would 'reserve all our rights to take any legal action in relation to this material'. The only consolation is that we were able to include another excellent piece by Peter Dorward.

What next? Well, the Canongate Prize looks set to go from strength to strength, with some major developments in the pipeline for the second year that will raise the profile of the competition significantly as well as the prize money.

I hope you enjoy the anthology and submit an entry for the competition in the coming year.

Jamie Byng, Publisher

TONI DAVIDSON

The Future Sound of Strangeness

Pain Dares to Risk
Flotation is about surface
Deprivation is about depth.
Explore your hidden fears, desires and dreams
with sensory deprivation
Nothing will not happen.

'*Inorganic quality of consciousness?* What is this shit, Enzo?'

'It's not shit.'

'*Once again I became the green dolphin?* That ain't shit?'

'It's what people say, isn't it?'

'*Moving into absolute void, no difference between minutes and millions of years?*'

'It's like I said people explore themselves in the tank and they need to find ways of expressing their experiences, their thoughts and impressions. New age analogies and mixed metaphors are the vocabulary of sensory deprivation. You know that as well as I do.'

Uri moved his head ten centimetres to the right, suddenly aware of each tendon in his neck pushing against the rubber mask, and looked in the direction of Enzo's voice. He was aware too of the shallow sound of his breath, an almost metallic echo reverberating inside his head. He knew that despite the mask Enzo would know he was drawing him a dirty look.

'We need these quotes Uri. They are the nitty gritty of the proposal. We need these examples to show that real people have undergone the SD experience and that the whole concept has gone beyond the confines of experimental, scientific research and into the real world.'

'There's precious little real about those people. Sounds like they watched *Altered States* one too many times and they now believe they are William Hurt, regressed and obsessed by native rituals, peyote infusions and gratuitous nudity. That not going to persuade a bunch of suits in the Citadel now is it?'

'It might. They want vox pop opinions all the better heard if referenced back to some celluloid glamour. The elected ones are of a new generation, more willing to admit to popular culture as an influence if not on them then certainly their electorate. The image of SD cultivated by William and other pseudo and neo-hippies can be easily transported into the new millennium and private enterprise shared with new age ideals, spawned from young talent, may well be the clincher.'

'*Immigrant* young talent, Enzo, don't forget that.'

'We are all citizens of the world, Uri.'

'Oh yeah, *I* forgot that.'

Uri tried to decide whether he felt hot or cold. He knew the temperature of the water. Both of them had taken care to maintain the temperature at 34.5°C in the tank, not allowing for even tiniest variation. Consistency after all was everything. A cold shiver or a warm glow would only be a distraction in the tank. After a number of failed prototypes the mask seemed to be working and the refinements they had made to the breathing apparatus had enabled him to submerge himself completely while the rest of his body hung naked and suspended in the water solution. He felt entirely at ease, untroubled by the pressure of gravity. He could understand why people reported this eerie situation as being completely natural.

'Well, I'm glad you're doing the pitch, not me, Enzo.'

'I'm pitching, you're floating?'

'That's the idea isn't it?'

'Yeah, sure, but we've got to be on the ball about this Uri, I mean really on the ball. We've got one shot at it and if we don't get it right then you know what's going to happen, don't you . . .?'

'Ah, the MacLean and MacLeod factor.'

'Exactly. If we pitch either side of MSP expectation they're going to reject immigrant innovation and go with the homegrown talent.'

'Aye, its a fearsome reel that we dance . . . You can just imagine those fuckers with their "sporran immersed in tank" graphic plastering the town with cheesy posters declaring "Immerse yourself in Scottish Culture, Come to MacLean and MacLeod Flotation World".'

'It's corny but it could work.'

'Corny? If those elected fuckers fall for that shit then I might as well stay in here for the rest of my life. SD will save me! SD will keep me from realising what a shit-hole I live in, a shit-hole infected by a squirming, fickle humanity who think it is better to float in a solarium cum hairdresser cum flotarium than to get to the core of who or what they really are.'

'It's quite a package they're offering.'

'Oh yeah, real attractive. Thirty quid for half an hour tanning, twenty minute floating and ten for a quick trim. They're skimming the surface of what really counts.'

'I know that, you know that, but we have to convince the elected ones that what we're offering is a more meaningful, more lasting contribution to the fabric of this new society. We are changing while acknowledging what we were; we are the new William Hurts without the drugs, neuroses or the emotional immaturity to keep a good solid relationship working.'

'Now that, Enzo, is good, but what about the drugs, eh? Mention SD and the elected ones are going to start worrying about old images of multiple drug deaths and wasted youth.'

After dozens of times in the tank which they had both constructed in the cellar of their basement, tenement flat, Uri had become aware of the different stages involved in SD, enough to be lucid and descriptive about them when they met their first paying customer. For about the first hour, the days detritus was present, the comings and goings of impressions and problems whirled around his head. After this there came an acceptance of where he was, a seeping sense of both relaxation and subtle amazement. But during the next hour he felt a shift away from this quasi-relaxed feel. A tension developed stemming from what SD

accounts refer to as 'stimulus-action hunger' and suddenly a range
of subtle but powerful self-stimulated reflexes came into play. Uri
had felt one finger start to brush another, a strange skin on skin
sensation and he became hyper aware of the slow movement of
water over his skin, the involuntary counting of his eyes, blinking
movements and many other seemingly trivial auto-reflexes which
would have gone for the most part unnoticed in the world outside
the tank. This was the testing window and during his first self-
encounters in the tank, Uri had been forced to leave, often with a
desperate and sudden need welling up inside him. Then, naked
and dripping, he would feel suddenly alone and small, reflecting
with disbelief on the basic power of the tiniest of sensations, the
fragile strength of mental resolve.

'The drug issue has to be tackled head on. There will, as
you say, be a tendency to link sensory deprivation with
stimulants. Obviously the other side of the William Hurt
factor is that although the elected ones may be keen on the
innovation, the reassuring hype that they are in tune with the
hip and the happening, they will remember Hurt freaking
out, daubing himself with body paints and going into a
convulsed, post-Janis Joplin jive. We have to counter this
association quickly and efficiently. Sensory deprivation is the
antidote to drugs; to the recreational therapy of getting high,
of tuning in and dropping out. In the new millennium, in the
new world far away from sweaty clubs or smacked up
schemes, SD will replace the use of illegal highs with natural
self-discovery. We will not be peddling safer or legal drugs –
we will be pitching the idea that sensory deprivation will
actually remove the desire for such taboo activities, that it will

replace by spiritual journeying the need for such artifice. One session in the tank will have the kids chucking their pills down the pan.'

'What about the "green dolphin" factor?'

'We don't mention that.'

After the first few sessions, Uri managed to get past the stimulus hunger stage. He knew each and every session in the tank would have its own components, its own personal and emotional dynamic. In fact during the second session as he and Enzo were still working on the first prototype which sprung the occasional leak and veered wildly in its temperature, he had assumed that directed thinking would be a good way of spending the time – as though time was something that had to be acknowledged in the tank, a bargainable quality that had to be considered. Like many friends and investors who had been involved over the past few months as the tank had gone through various stages of development he had thought it would be a good opportunity for some peace and quiet to solve some problems and dilemmas – in his case how to convince the newly elected MSPs that SD was a prime example of New Age, third way enterprise to be lauded and shouted from the rooftops. But his fellow testers had reported that the tank wasn't the place for such humdrum decision making. After the tense early stages, many people reported shifting away from this directed thinking to more emotional and fantastical reveries. Indeed, Seltin, a friend of some years, could barely bring himself to explain what he had gone through and had rushed to dry himself, an expression across his face that could be best described as elated panic.

'I still think we should go with our original idea.'

'Which original idea was that?'

'We pitch it to MSP McIver at the shop.'

'The place is a building site, Enzo.'

'All the better for him to see that we are both serious about our proposal and that we need money to complete its obvious commercial possibilities.'

'But it means that we'll have to set the tank up in less than pristine conditions. That might not be encouraging to him.'

'Maybe, but what choice do we have? We can't pack up the tank and all the equipment and traipse off to the Citadel and set up there can we? No, it's better in the shop.'

'You're the boss Enzo.'

'We're partners, Uri, fifty-fifty all the way.'

'Yeah, but you're the one with the bright ideas.'

'Well said. So, here's another one. We invite MSP McIver to deprive himself of his senses.'

Uri knew how his friend Seltin felt. He had understood the look he had seen on his face. It was an expression he saw repeated time and time again. This wonderful delirium was the reason why he had come to believe in what Enzo had rushed to convince him of after a six-month visit to California. Enzo had toured different scientific Institutes that were experimenting with SD and memory theories as well as visiting the commercial floatariums where new agers and surfers worked on their psyches accompanied by essential oils and bench presses. It was obvious to Enzo that there could be a bridge between the ultra scientific and the relentlessly superficial. The SD Shop was the natural result. And if Uri needed any more convincing then Enzo's lyrical

wax about spiritual realignment and thick profit margins was
more than enough. But he knew, putting all that aside, that the
simplest truths were often the most convincing, and the simple
truth about SD was that it gave you time and space to spend
with yourself that would never occur in a normal, waking
environment.

'I don't think so, Enzo.'

'Why?'

'Because, I don't see McIver blending with the green dolphin, know what I mean? He's going to take one look at the state of the shop and make a whole bunch of premature conclusions.'

'Easy. The debris just shows we've got a working idea. We get him past that, lure him in with peaceful new age concepts linked closely . . .'

'Yeah, I've heard the pitch but you are seriously suggesting that McIver is going to get his kit off and suspend his rump in the saline simply because he wants to give us a grant to further this spiritual lifeline?'

'In essence yes. Think about it. You know his connection with MacLean and MacLeod, you know they will have regaled him with a very similar business plan, beautifully desk topped and spattered with gratuitous national identity icons but without the zest of experimentation, without the jolt of the new. This is our edge that our competitors simply do not have. They are old money, they are relying on national and hereditary links to get the grant whereas we are about opportunity and enterprise, a chip off the new block.'

'What if he says no?'

'Politicians love the opportunity to show off – think of all those photographs of suits in hardhats stuffing burgers down children's throats or riding earth diggers. It's the kissing babies rule. Politicians can't afford not to.'

Uri had wondered about music in the tank, shifting between a desire for the silence to be continued and an urge for an ambient wash, a bit of Eno or Satie, something to take him out of his body. But then, these very thoughts were symptomatic of the reasons for being in the tank, what was happening both to the mind and to the body. In fact, if he was honest, he had tried when Enzo wasn't around, had immersed himself in both the tank and in some synthetic whale nonsense but the self-consciousness battle that preempted most initial experiences in SD was a battle fought and lost very quickly. He found too much to dislike about the music, his ability to know what he disliked was heightened by the SD environment and it was all still too close to caftans and herbal instincts. No, in the end, his recommendation to their prospective customers was to take nothing into the tank, to simply revel in silence for the silence would soon become crowded with mind noise . . .

*   *   *

Uri could tell McIver was nervous. On the surface of course he was all smiles and handshakes, his moon face beaming at Enzo who apologised for the mess in the shop with just the right amount of humility while playing up the working twelve hours a day line to shore up the MSP's belief that they were working hard for what they cared about. Something Enzo knew McIver would want to identify with. But as Enzo explained the nitty-gritty of the tank's concept and working procedure uncertainty cracked the smile a little, and the foot shuffle began as did the rotation of the takeaway cafe latte in his chubby fingers.

'So have many people tried out the prototype tank then?'

There was reassurance to be had of course in the number of people who had been immersed and survived.

'Many times, and in its various stages as we adjusted the water temperature, the saline balance etcetera our friends have been called in to create a wide database of reactions and criticisms – very important if we are to perfect both the experience and the tank itself.'

Uri watched McIver walk slowly around the tank, surreptitiously checking for leaks or for any other danger signs. It was clear that he was shit scared of doing this and yet having come this far he knew it would look bad to back out. No politician, as Enzo had said, would shy away from a proffered baby. As McIver warily circled the tank, Enzo launched into section 21 of his pitch, the part which might appeal to the busy elected one,

'. . . it is a natural deconditioning tool since while the customer is floating he or she will be completely separated from the usual, domestic interaction with the world; so many people are transfixed by routine that to be suddenly relieved of this hypnotic repetition is to be freed both in body and mind – it's worth mentioning that the commercial SD pioneers like Zen-r-chi noted that perceptions and sensations take place against a background of muscular activity and the lack of gravity within the tank greatly decreases sensitivity and awareness of external reality factors like stress, eating disorders and . . . (with perfect timing, Enzo leaned slightly closer to McIver's shoulder) family problems.'

Enzo had done a little homework, enough to learn that at the age of 41, McIver had chalked up two marriages, three children and was now just six months into his third ring-bound relationship. It was a safe bet that Enzo might catch something with the skimming motion of his words. Unfortunately, his brief glance at McIver's biography and family links had also revealed one disturbing fact. He was related to MacLean by marriage and if there was one thing Enzo and Uri knew about it was the importance of family links, the skewered, pink-fingered handshakes and the red marks on men's bare backs as they embraced. It occurred to them both that McIver was playing the politician, ingratiating himself with The SD Shop simply to seem democratic, allowing for choice while having already made up his mind where the funds were going to go. Of course they didn't know this for sure, he was a new breed of politician whose blood ties might not lead to backhanders. They had to give him a chance. More than McIver knew, they had nothing to lose.

Within ten minutes of his arrival McIver was down to his boxer shorts and vest, deciding which goggles to wear, the final decisive act before all reality thinking mechanisms were suspended. Enzo held each set out to him.

'The *Mindshed* goggles are entirely opaque and allow you to open and close your eyes while the *Esten* goggles are translucent and are a little like having halved ping-pong balls placed across the eyes. Within the tank there are distinguishable differences between the two. I recommend the *Esten* goggles for your first immersion.'

McIver slowly went into the water. His moon face was oozing undisguisable concern now and yet he still went ahead, a testament, Uri thought, to his dedication to his job. Enzo fitted the mask and adjusted the breathing tube so that McIver was happy with the mix and had got used to the slightly strange inhaling/exhaling protocols that an immersion in an SD tank demanded. There were usually a fair amount of explanations and exercises to take place before a client went in for the first time. But with a nod McIver did not see, Enzo and Uri went straight in at the deep end. Or rather McIver did.

With a noticeable metallic clang the lid was closed and again Enzo and Uri exchanged a glance, a broad smile and they rushed forward to greet each other with a high five. Then, without saying a word they turned and opened the small viewing slit in the side of the tank. McIver's moon face was enveloped by the mask, the tube giving, as it did everyone who occupied the tank, an alien appearance, a space-age embryonic look . . . no matter how many times Uri had seen a body float inside the tank he couldn't get bored of the sight. Enzo and Uri drew close to each other, their heads vying for space. For a moment neither of them spoke and Uri knew that Enzo was waiting for him to break the ice, to take the step that both of them knew they wanted to take. So Uri started it.

'The voices first then?'

'I think that would be an appropriate place to start.'

'You sure about this?'

'Absolutely. This fat cat had made his mind up before he came in, you saw it in his eyes, in the way he paid lip service to our pitch. He, like so many of his kind, is on an experience junket, try anything, say anything, mean nothing. It's time he, shall we say, faced the music.'

'Corny but gloriously true.'

Enzo had taken a while to adapt and fix the tiny ear pieces to the mask McIver was wearing, it had taken a combination of security technology and maritime ingenuity to come up with them but then Enzo had a gift for adaptability both in practical and intellectual terms. The DAT was already set up and with a grin he started it. There was an artistry about this particular tape, an imaginative response to Enzo's trip to California where he had heard a multitude of aural soundscapes used for SD. They had recorded the voice of McIver along with many others of his fellow MSPs during one of their long, long debates. In California, the use of multi-tracked voices was used in order to create a harmonious, Koyanniskatsi-like soundscape of human experience, the soft voices of intoned prayer, the steady pulse of Gregorian chants, the whispers of dreaming children, but Enzo of course immediately saw a different use for the context, an altogether more malevolent and disturbing use. This, more than a few pseudo new agers floating in their salined musk, was the real commercial opportunity presenting itself to Enzo and Uri. It was the new Silicon Glen. International companies intent on weeding out timewasters and short termers would welcome The Shop's SD approach as part of their senior level recruitment package; the research industry would welcome the opportunity for the milieu testing of various pharmaceuticals while law enforcement agencies would find it hard not to be impressed with the persuasive uses of SD. They had already had enquiries.

Enzo played the tape low first of all and there was a twitch from McIver inside the tank. The voices were multi tracked and dubbed so that the volume and complexity of voice intonation would increase as the minutes passed. They noted, as they squeezed against the glass, that after ten minutes, McIver's head was shaking from side to side, as though trying to escape the cascading sound of his colleagues filling his head. Uri made sure he caught it all on DVC. A useful promotional aid.

'Do you think it makes sense to him Enzo?'

'It is possible that he is allowing himself to think that his hearing is playing tricks on him, convincing himself what MacLeod and MacLean have been telling him all along. SD truly is a unique experience. He may well not want to cave in too easily since he will not want to appear weak or feeble-minded.

'What about the O_2 part.'

'It's about the right moment for that . . .'

'Didn't he say he was asthmatic?'

'He expressed some concern, I believe.'

Enzo bent down to the flow regulators and very slowly reduced the amount of air feeding down the tube. The effect was almost immediate. McIver's body convulsed a little and any sense of calm that may have been in place before was quickly eroded by the lapping saline against the metal tank.

Uri noticed the flashing red light beside the flow

regulator that indicated that the air supply was insufficient while the blue light beside kicked in almost at the same time. 'Seems he's found the panic button.'

'Clever boy. Okay lets give him some air and then start with some suitable images.'

This was the part which both of them had been looking forward to. Enzo had seen some incredible sights in California. The cutting edge new agers there had decided it wasn't enough simply to take hallucinogens and immerse themselves for hours on end – this was strictly for weekenders. The goatee-bearded blonds seeking extra thrills beyond spills and pills arranged for projections to be shown on to their *Esten* goggles. The resulting effect of images as diverse as thirty foot waves crashing millimetres in front of their eyes to fairly serious macro vagina shots had to be seen and felt to be believed. The images weren't just seen by the eyes but pressed into the mind, the *Esten* goggles channelling the blurred images onto the retina and beyond.

Enzo focussed the projector into a tight spot on the wall, away from the tank.

'Exit the voices and put on some thrash.'

Uri changed the DAT and watched McIver gyrate, his arms shaking while his legs buckled and straightened. Ironically with enough funding they could have wired McIver up to a pulse rate monitor and entertained themselves as they watched some blip slalom but Enzo made do with the potent effects of the projector adjusting its angle so that a stream of light poured into the tank, a beam cutting into the darkness.

'What did you choose for today's show, Enzo?'

'The Reporting Scotland footage of the inaugural debate at the Citadel.'

'Nice choice.'

'I thought so. McIver gives a particularly riveting performance, plenty of gusto and verve and the best part is just about to come.'

They shifted their attention from McIver's blubbery, writhing body to the small viewing screen. There was an altogether different McIver, suited, respectable and in full flow. Seems he was keen to emphasise the role of new and innovative enterprise in Scotland and felt that small businesses like, by way of example, that of the Floatariums run by young, go-getting partners MacLeod and MacLean, should be given a leg up in the new Scotland, that youthful enthusiasm should be applauded whatever those of different generations might think. Context, he said with aplomb, is everything.

CHRIS DOLAN

Redlegs

Most of Barbados lies flat on the water, a polished coral jewel set in the lapping lazuli of the Caribbean Sea. But the Scotland district, like my own country, rises into stark chiselled highlands in the north.

I decide to explore the area on my day off and, as if to make me feel at home, the rain's bucketing down. I'm the only passenger on the number 22 bus trundling through sodden hills, on my way to visit some National Trust gardens. I'm sitting up with the driver who's going to let me off at the right stop. He's been chatting away to me, but I can only understand about a third of what he's saying – that northern accent's a killer. I'm about to step out into the deluge, when he says it's hardly a day for wandering round gardens. Why not stay on and come back to town on the return run? He introduces himself as Sylvan (I think) and says he'll point out some of the sights. Up the road a bit is the infamous bandit country (Sylvan swears blind the highwaymen never attack buses); he'll show me lime trees, akkie bushes and mangoes. He reaches down beside his seat and pulls out two bottles of Carib lager, cracks them open and I sit back to enjoy a two dollar trip through a miniature, but today magnificently rainy, rain-forest.

Little Scotland and Big Scotland have more in common than you'd think. We share some history, a lot of family names, a not disimilar geology and, on a day like this, bucketsful of rain. There are loads of places in the New World with echoes of the old, but this particular island has a very special story to tell. A dark whisper. A warning.

Sylvan veers off the 22 route and takes me to a high viewpoint which could easily be The Queen's View looking over the Lomond hills, except that there's sweat trickling down my back as well as rain. A woman waves the bus down and gets on, unconcerned that the 22 is nowhere near its regular location or time. Sylvan gives her a bottle of beer, and she joins the tour. We get talking about the Redlegs – the natives of the Scotland district.

– Redlegs – Sylvan explains – because their ancestors used to wear kilts and got their white knees burned by the sun.

Sylvan's the most amiable man alive but like all black Bajans, he's dismissive of the 'Backra Johnnies'.

– Back-row. Used to be poor whites was made to sit at the back of church.

My lady travelling companion leans towards me confidentially:

– Respectable black families didn't want nothing to do with white trash then, John Ross.

Everyone calls me John Ross here, on the assumption that most visitors are as American as JR Ewing. Although Bajans are surrounded by poor whites – and in the Scotland district the Backras really are poor – they still associate incomer whites with the richest man from American telly.

I keep getting taken for a missionary, too. Missionaries apparently wear white suits like the one I've got on. Maybe that was why I was getting the free bus tour. Out of respect for Christian evangelism.

What I can't understand, I tell them, is why there's not more sense of solidarity between blacks and poor whites? Both communities have had a hard struggle. Both have been oppressed by colonial powers. Both were uprooted against their will from their homelands and have suffered hunger, slavery and disease on foreign shores, under ruthless masters. The Redlegs are descended from a potent gallimaufry of Celtic rebels. Scots and Irish Covenanters who fought against Cromwell, malcontents who stood against the Duke of Monmouth – the lucky ones who escaped death being sent here to work out their short lives as slaves. Others are the destitute heirs of two generations of Jacobites, deported and indentured, sold for ten pounds a head. The history of Scotland – big Scotland – can be traced in local family names. Highland-sounding MacLeods and Macdonalds and Lowland Maxwells. Each one with a story to tell of Clearances, vicious landlords, oppression at home. Irish names hint at famine. Welsh and English of religious and political intolerance. Some of today's Redlegs, certainly, will be descended from deported convicts, bauds and thieves from the British seventeenth-century meanstreets. More are the offspring of brave stalwarts who packed up the little they had, survived the crossing, and sold themselves into slavery in the hope of becoming respectable homesteaders after their contracted five years. The system that had impoverished them back home, however, continued to impoverish most of them here.

So why aren't the rich white colonising families the common enemy of blacks and 'backras' alike?

– Difference is – says Sylvan – we had enough pride in our race to rebel. Backra Johnnies don't have pride in themselves.

Further study of surnames offers another clue to racial disharmony. British Empire names given to black Bajans are tell-tale signs of old ownership, rape and slave-driving. But there was once a time when poor whites *were* proud, and had the spirit and solidarity to fight alongside black comrades against the oppressor. From the 1680's to the early eighteenth century a number of plots and insurrections, jointly planned by black slaves and white servants, were discovered and defeated. Elsewhere in the Caribbean white peasants and workers joined forces with slave leaders to further the cause of emancipation and equality. But in the Scotland district, and in the white trash shanties around Bridgetown, the 'back-row' mentality set in quickly and deep. What had seemed radical back home – fighting for a Stewart rather than a Hanovarian for instance – was regressive and backward in the new world. Their partiality for kings, and loyalty to the old mother country imbued them with an unhealthy kind of nationalism. Scrabbling for work and status in their new country, they saw the energetic and inventive black slave as a competitor. And in the long run, an altogether more successful competitor.

The black majority – ninety-eight per cent of Barbados's population – threw up radical leaders like John Wickham and Clement Payne. In 1966 Errol Barrow won independence for Barbados. By and large, the rich whites upped and offed. Bodily, at least – some of the best land and most profitable businesses are still run from abroad by absent landlords. Still, the first thing you notice on the taxi ride from Barbados airport is a proud, belligerent statue depicting slaves tearing off their chains.

I'm half-way through a six-week stint working with young Bridgetown delinquents, on behalf of UNESCO. The 'homeboys' – another American borrowing – are all bedecked with the insignia of black assertiveness. Baseball caps, hair shaved to the temples, heavy gold chains and tiny peering shades. They wear it all like scars they intend to avenge. I haven't seen much vengeance being wreaked however – Milngavie's scarier on a Saturday night than Bridgetown. I've been to remand centres, youth clubs, and downtown discos which the honky tourists avoid like the plague and, although your average young Bajan might look like Tupak Shakur in a nasty mood, in fact they're all bafflingly polite and are more likely to brandish conservative morals at you than a blade. Not long after I'd arrived in Barbados, I'd hopped on a route taxi (minibuses which you pick up any-where on the street – no need to look out for them, you can hear their dub and ragga vibes pounding a mile away). The driver looked every inch a *gangsta*. Two accomplices sat on either side of me. I felt like Jimmy Krankie at a Harlem Globetrotters' reunion. A moment of pure white panic. Once they'd elicited from me what I was doing in Bridgetown wearing a suit and being white, they pummelled me with discourses on the breakdown of family values, disaffection with the established churches and the leniency of the penal system. As I got off, one guy shouted over the music:

– Sure you're not a missionary?

– Honest.

– Well you should be!

The door slammed and the bus blared off, bruising the night.

Sylvan's taken Mrs Braithwaite, our fellow traveller, and me back to his house for a bite to eat. He's unconcerned about what the depot might think, or any waiting passengers further down the line. Thelma, his wife, doesn't seem put out either by this sudden picnic party. Their house is a rough-hewn, brightly painted old *chattle* (wooden) construction that seems to have sprouted naturally out of the mangrove, sweet orchids and grapefruit trees that twine around it. Sylvan's pulled up outside and Thelma has brought plates-full of fried flying fish, eddoes and *coocoo*, a local cornmeal mash, out to us on the bus. We move on from beer to *mauby*, a drink made from steeped tree-bark. I climb down to stand out in the rain, enjoying the sauna-like feel of the hot air and hotter rain, looking up at the hills of Scotland. Sylvan, Thelma and Mrs Braithwaite don't comment – they're used to eccentric American evangelists.

There are still plenty of signs of poverty and Backra backwardness around, but the Scotland district's better than it once was. For a long time the Redleg villages were the saddest of sights. At the end of last century, Quintin Hogg wrote:

> It is a pitiable thing to see [the Redlegs] wandering about with some of the conceit of the white blood, but none of the energy of the European.

In the thirties, Patrick Leigh Fermor lamented

> the ragged white men . . . in the same humble plight as when
> they were first herded ashore.

I think about what Joshua Grant, a young Backra I'd met the weekend before, told me about the modern Redleg. We were on a Barbadian National Trust trek around the Atlantic side of the island, where sheer cliffs surge up over wild surf like ancient petrified waves. Maybe my brain just hadn't kicked in yet – the Trust's walks begin at 6 a.m. – but Joshua might as well have been speaking the ancient tongue of the Caribs. Sylvan's accent is bad enough and the Bridgetown kids demand some concentration, but Joshua, who for all the world looked like he was on a package holiday from Kirk-caldy, sounded like Shaggy on speed. With the help of a black interpreter, I got his gist: these days, Redlegs are doing it for themselves. The biggest shop downtown is Shepherd's, founded and run by a rags-to-riches Redleg. Other 'backras' run the island's car maintenance industry, and they're beginning to capitalise along with everyone else on tourism.

But for more than two centuries the Redlegs kept themselves to themselves, mired in hopeless poverty. While we stay-at-home Scots began to fight for our own culture and rights, our Bajan cousins grumbled and squabbled with the local blacks. Instead of cuddying up to the slave rebel leaders, furthering their joint objectives, the poor whites sank into a pit of jealousy and racism. When it came, Emancipation was a disaster, not a victory, for the Redlegs. In their new-found confidence the blacks began to take over the island for themselves. The whites had backed the wrong horse – wagered everything on colour instead of class. No wonder the victors relegated them to the back rows of churches.

So what made the difference? What made the blacks fight back, while the sons of Albion rebels sank into rancour and hatred? I was given a strong clue the night before embarking on Sylan's bus. Getting back on board, out of the rain, I rehearse with Sylvan and Mrs Braithwaite a cultural quandary I'd found myself in.

A friend had taken me to a club in St Lawrence Gap – an entire village of nothing but pubs and clubs built mainly for the tourists. Thankfully I was ushered past all the beach-bars crammed with sun-reddened and beer-crimsoned faces, and shunted off down a side street into a club patronised by laid-back locals. My companion, Lois, was the nearest thing to a Bajan aristocrat. Descended from a long line of Black Independence activists, half her family now held high positions in the government. For a Scots bumpkin like me, Lois is exotically well-groomed, immaculately dressed, and as fragile as a piece of porcelain.

Out on the open-air dance floor, everything seemed sedate enough. The dancers lined up shoulder-to-shoulder like they were about to do a line-dance. Then MC Grandmaster unleashed his jungle and soca thrashings. Ring-bang rhythms turned Little England – as the rest of Barbados, south of the Scotland district is known – into furious Africa, leaving me fretting that the fine porcelain in my care would be shattered amid the gyrations and flailing about. Suddenly the guy in front of Lois birled round so he was dancing face-to-face with her. She kept dancing, not making eye contact with him, but not backing off either. Then he moved in closer, until they were dancing groin-to-groin. Eye-contact was firmly established, the pair of them gyrated sensually, intimately, and I just didn't know where to look. What was I supposed to do in this predicament? Slope off quietly and not mention the incident the next day? Climb onto Lois's shoulders, get eye-to-eye with this guy and say back off pal? As it turned out, they danced and rubbed and ground while I slunked and loitered, then she walked off and he moved along the line.

Sylvan and old Mrs Braithwaite couldn't see the problem.

– They were just dancing, John Ross.

I said in *my* Scotland that's not dancing, it's shagging. Perhaps they were surprised at a missionary using such language. Maybe they thought it was just my evangelist convictions that had been offended by such an exhibitionist sexual display. Sylvan smiled and hopped back in his bus, got us all aboard for the final leg of the tour back up through Redleg country.

There can be no doubt that it was Africa and the African spirit that made the difference in the blacks' struggle against oppression. Neither Celtic nor class pride ignited the spirit of revolt amongst the Redlegs. The memory of freedom and nobility and racial dignity was on tap for the most oppressed Barbadians, but not for the poor whites. Most of the Backras have no idea where they come from. They've lost all contact with their past. The missing ingredients are memory and Africa. In an island which is almost entirely black-skinned, apart from the tourists and backras, there appears, at first glance, to be precious little of the spirit of Africa around. But it's there all right. It lies below the surface, just under the skin, and erupts when the right music, the right conditions for a battle, present themselves. The kids I'm working with in the 'hood glower with defiance. Sylvan and Mrs Braithwaite possess an enviable love of country and a hope for the future. Joshua agreed that the Redlegs had a lot to learn from African insurrectionist energy.

The number 22 reached Bridgetown four hours late. No-one seemed to mind. We three mutual voyagers made our fare-wells, me promising to get the same bus next week.

– Can't promise you another free tour, friend.

Back at my apartment, I couldn't get the ramshackle, downtrodden villages of the Redlegs out my mind. I sat on the veranda watching an Atlantic storm brewing up darkly over the ocean, trying to work out the message Little Scot-land has for Big Scotland. What happens to a people who have been severed from their own history? A once-proud nationalist and idealistic people degenerate into a fatalist and forgotten one, that's what. Maybe we have more in common with our Backra cousins than we'd like to think. Maybe we could do with a bit of ring-bang defiance ourselves.

From my apartment window I look over to the Caribbee Plaza across the bay. The Caribbee's the hotel they put me up in when I first arrived. But I couldn't stand it. Couldn't handle the AOR muzak, Typical Bajan Evenings and Fun Excursions. I wonder now if the Backras really have had their day – or if they're just being replaced by another kind of Redleg. Those well-off holidaymakers across the way there, huddled together, not from the encroaching storm, but from the life outside their hotel complex. Hardly venturing to taste *coocoo* or *mauby*, seldom bumping and grinding to ragga and kaiso, uninterested in meeting a Joshua or a Lois or a Sylvan, they'll never discover that, behind brochure Barbados, there's a wild and turbulent Little Africa of wild surf, soaked gullies, rebelliousness and black pride.

They say that in a few years there'll be no trace left of the Redlegs. Nothing more than the fleeting sensation you get in the morning after a bad dream. I decide I'm going to go back up into the Scotland district, before it disappears forever, note and record what I can. Why should I worry, though, about the loss of that failed and bitter community? Because they're people, I suppose. Long-lost cousins. And because at root, a long time ago, they were strong, radical leaders. Because what happened to them is a warning it would be perilous to ignore . . .

The Redlegs are the past. Amongst the holidaymakers across the way undoubtedly there will be Scots. Scots from across the Atlantic. New Scots, on the verge of a new millenium, a new country. The past is here, on this beautiful island, to be be learned from. Those new, cancer-risking Redlegs in the Caribbee are in danger of becoming every bit as defeated as the white trash up in the mountains. The Caribbee, and all the other swanky hotels on the island reek of segregation. Of money speaking louder than community, humanity. Tomorrow night I'll head north, see if I can still hear echoes of Covenanter and Jacobite courage, homesteader grit. Tonight, I switch off the light and listen to the new Redlegs over the bay, trapped in their exclusive package tours. Poor whites.

ANNE DONOVAN
Millennium Babe

e-mail

DATE: 1.1.2000   00:07:09

FROM: bmacreadie@qmhosp.nhs.glasgow

TO: rhsmith@sick.kids.nhs.london

It's a girl! 3.88 kg, apgar 8, normal birth after 5 hr labour.
Mother and baby both doing well.

e-mail

DATE: 1.1.2000   00:024:08

FROM: rhsmith@sick.kids.nhs.london

TO: bmacreadie@qmhosp.nhs.glasgow

OK you win. Our first didn't show till 00:11:31.

Front Page of the *Daily Record* (second edition)
1.1.2000

GLASGOW'S MILLENNI-MUM!

As bells rang in the millennium, thirty-three-year-old
Elspeth Scott gave birth to a baby girl in the Queen Mum's
Hospital, Glasgow. She's the first baby born in the new era,
not just in Scotland, but in Europe.

This new flower of Scotland weighed in at a healthy 8lb 8oz and has a mop of dark hair. Callie for short, her full name will be Caledonia Scott.

The Herald Diary

3.1.2000

A reader who wishes to remain anonymous sent us this conversation, overheard, he says, in the Vicky Bar, Saltmarket:

Punter A: Caledonia! Caledonia! Whit kind ae a bloody name is that, for fucksake. Caledonia. Whit kindae parents would name their wean efter a brewery?

Punter B: Bloody sponsorship, that'll be it. Sponsorin the millennium baby. Some folk wid dae anythin fur money, so they wid.

Punter A: Aye but could they no huv got it sponsored by Mothercare or sumpn. They didnae huvtae name it efter a brewery, that's no fair on the wean.

Punter C: Whit the hell are youse talkin aboot? Bloody ignorant, that's whit yes ur. Caledonia is Scotland, Scotland, oor nation. Whit better name could ye cry yer wean?

Punter A: Oh aye, so it is, Caledonia. At's right. Just like the advert, mind, wi thon Frankie Miller song.

Punter B: Aw aye. Caledonia . . .

Fax

TO: UK Operations, Edinburgh sub-branch, Caledonia
        Spring Water Company
FROM: Head Office, Caledonia Spring Water Company,
        Seattle
DATE: 3.1.2000   11.34   p1 of 1

Authorised to offer a further twenty-five thousand dollars on top of current offer. Confirmation now received she's the first millennium baby in northern hemisphere.

Record of Telephone Conversation

TO: James McIntyre, Edinburgh sub-branch manager
FROM: Darryl J. Tracker, President, Caledonia Spring Water Company
DATE: 3.1.2000   12.45

DJT: Whaddya mean, she doesn't want it? Who else is bidding? We can raise them, I mean with a name like Caledonia this is too good to miss.

JM: I'm sorry, Mr Tracker. The mother has apparently ruled out all sponsorship deals altogether. It's not a question of money.

DJT: It's always a question of money. Try again. No, on second thoughts, I'll send in Artemis Fleming-Gould. A woman's touch. She'll be able to make her see that it's actually in her child's best interests. What kind of mother refuses the chance to make her child a millionaire? It's criminal.

JM: I'm afraid you won't be able to do that, Mr Tracker. The woman has taken out some kind of legal proceedings, banning anyone from even speaking to her about sponsorship deals.

DJT: We'll see about that, McIntyre. There's always a way round these things.

Card (tasteful, Bellini Madonna and Child, the Burrell Collection)

TO: Ms E. Scott. Queen Mother's Hospital
FROM: Scottish Parliament, signed by all party leaders

DATE: 4.1.2000

Congratulations from us all on the new arrival. We are
delighted that Britain's first citizen of the new era is a Scot
(and a Scott!). We hope you and Caledonia are well.

Deliveries
5.1.2000

*Items delivered to the Queen Mother's Hospital and accepted on
behalf of Caledonia Scott:*

Snowsuit in the Scott tartan, donated by B. Scott, Bothwell

Set of Sir Walter Scott's novels, donated by Midlothian
branch of the Scott Appreciation Society

Teatowel with the Caledonia Canal printed on it donated
by Mrs Frances Scott, Arbroath

Toy Scottie dog donated by Scottoys, Stirling

Miniature silver quaich donated by Silverscots, Glencoe

Hand-knitted, pure new wool bootees, donated by Scot-
socks, Shetland

*Items refused on behalf of Caledonia Scott. To be uplifted from
Store and delivered to various charities:*

Pushchairs, car seats, baby clothing, nappies, baby toiletries, toys from various manufacturers

Chocolates, flowers, ladies' toiletries, clothing

Transcript of Press Conference
Queen Mother's Hospital
DATE: 6.1.2000   10.30

PR Manager, Hospital Trust:

Good morning, ladies and gentlemen. The format of this

morning's press briefing will be as follows: Mr MacNeill, Ms Scott's solicitor, will read a statement. Then Ms Scott and baby Caledonia will do a photo-session with the official photographer. Copies will be issued to all representatives of the media and no unauthorised photography will be allowed. Two journalists from BBC Scotland and STV will be permitted three prepared questions each as agreed yesterday. Neither Ms Scott, Mr MacNeill nor any member of the Hospital Trust staff will answer further questions from journalists and any failure to observe this protocol will result in the immediate termination of the press conference.

*   *   *

Caledonia Scott's Diary
1.1.2014

A folder full of cuttings. She said she thought it was time for me to see them, maybe help make some sense of it all. The only bit that makes sense now is this wee blurred photie. Dark fuzzy hair, huge big eyes, blue, like all babies. That's me; the rest, media hype.

Journalists are vicious, everybody wants to make money out of you. There was always some photographer trying to get a snap of me on my first day at school or playing in the swing park. Lawyers, protection orders. What the hell made her think she could protect me from it?

'Hen, ah wis just tryin tae dae ma best fur ye.'

'Aye ma, heard it.'

'Ah didnae want ye tae be pestered. Ah wanted you tae have an ordinary life.'

An ordinary life. When you're the first baby in the northern hemisphere born into the millennium. In Scotland. Where we'd just got our first parliament for 300 years. Oh aye. And what do you cry her – Caledonia Scott. Just so's she'll be ordinary.

Who wants to be ordinary? Weans spend their time dreaming that they've been adopted and they're really princesses in disguise – it's in the books. I was about seven when I discovered that my ma had actually turned down all these firms that wanted to give us money, she'd denied me the chance to be a millionaire. When you're seven, being a millionaire just means having as many sweeties as you can eat, but still. Even then I thought she was daft, but by the time I was thirteen, I could've murdered her. Her and her bloody principles.

'It's too dear, Callie.'

'Everybody else has got them.'

'Ah don't care, we cannae afford these designer claes, ah bought you the trainers you wanted and that's it tae the end of the month.'

'You make me sick, d'you know that?'

'Callie . . .'

'I could've been rich, but naw, you had to turn down the money. You're above all that. You're bloody purer than pure.'

'Callie ah'm no discussin this in a shop. Ah've explained how we thought it wis best.'

'We . . . who is this royal we?'

'Your faither and me, Callie.'

'Oh aye, mystery man. Who's he when he's at hame? Anybody'd think you had the virgin birth all over again. How come I've never seen him, never heard from him, naebody knows who he is, in spite of all the detectives and reporters?'

'Callie, ah've tellt you there are reasons and some day you'll unnerstaun. It's because of oor principles, its because we care aboot Scotland, it's no aboot money. It's aboot oor country and who you are.'

That's just the point – who am I? That's the topic for the essay I'm supposed to be writing now. That daft student teacher that's taking us the now gave it to us for homework over the Christmas holidays. Her wi her jingly-jangly bracelets and her colour-printed worksheet – Helpful suggestions for writing:

Who am I?

Write about what you feel constitutes your identity in the world.

In what ways are you influenced by your family, interests, beliefs, friends?

How do the new powers devolved to the Scottish Parliament this year affect your sense of yourself as a Scot?

We've got to write at least two pages. Mad Lizzie says she's going to cover two pages with *I am Lizzie Nicol* written over and over again.

Who Am I?

Where do I start? My family? I know who my mum is, but I've never known my father and this folder of junk doesn't take me any nearer. My name is Scott but that's a kid-on. My gran's maiden name was Scott and my mum changed her name to Scott when she knew I was going to be born in the millennium. Caledonia Scott. How can you have an identity of your own with a name like that? I've often thought of changing it when I'm old enough. Shona's mum became a Buddhist recently and she's changed her name to something unpronounceable. Shona's mortified cos she won't answer to Mrs Anderson any more, not even for parents' nights. That's worse than my mum, though I hate the way she always says, 'It's Ms, not Mrs,' in a nippy tone. I suppose all parents are embarrassing in their own way. I wish she wouldn't keep pushing this Scots language thing, though. I mean, writing absence notes in Scots for God's sake! And looking up the Scots dictionary and Thesaurus for even more obscure versions of words. The teachers'll think she's illiterate. I mean I do speak that way sometimes myself when I'm at home or if I'm with my pals and I want to be funny, but there's a time and place for everything. She keeps on at me about losing my 'mither tongue'. She nearly went mental the other day when I said Maria had grassed on Bushra.

'The word is clype, no grass. You've got a guid Scots tongue in yer heid, ma lass and you should be pruid o it.'

In front of Angie, as well. Gie's a break, ma.

So family's no use. What about interests?

Music. Art. Art's the most important though. It's the one thing I'm really good at, the one thing I can lose myself in. I want to do something with it when I leave school, maybe go to Art school. But I can't write about that, it's just something I do. When you try to talk about it the words get in the way.

*

Beliefs. That's a big one. Haven't a clue, really. I'm not very religious though I wouldn't like to say there definitely isn't a God. And I'm not political, totally scunnered by politics after having it drummed into me all my life. How wonderful Scotland is, how we've got to make her A Real Nation Again. And it does sound wonderful when you're wee, then one day you realise these folk your ma talks to at rallies and brings home after meetings are presumably the ones who'll be in charge of this Scottish nation. Well just look at them: wee wifies, big daft boys, sleekit wee grey-suits and, worst of all, the smart young women in red suits wi big shooders. And there's Our Parliament. Well, they don't seem to me to be any different from that lot at Westminster.

So that leaves friends. That doesn't help either. I've got friends of course, pals, folk I hang about with, Angie and Bushra and Lucy especially. But that's it. We hang out. We go into town, we go to parties, we sometimes get drunk. But I don't think they've got much to do with anything that's central to my identity. Maybe the opposite. When I'm with them I probably feel less sure of who I am, less confident, I don't really know what my views are till they've spoken first, especially Angie. With my ma I'm dead confident, renta-mouth, but that's because I'm reacting to her all the time, trying to be different I suppose. At the end of the day I don't know who I am at all.

*   *   *

Letter to Caledonia Scott

to be opened on 1.1.2021

Dear Callie,

This day is your twenty-first birthday and ah hope it will be a truly happy one. Ah thocht that this wid be a fittin time tae tell ye some things that ye have aye wanted to ken aboot yer history.

The wan thing ah canna tell ye is yer faither's name. All ah can say is that he is a weel-kent politician (and guy politik in hissel). Ah ken this will start ye jalousin but ah think ye'll no get it richt. He's no a likely candidate for this position.

At the time ye were conceived we were richt in love but he was merriet. We never planned yer birth but when we realised that ye were like to be born roon the millennium time we were hert-gled as it seemed tae be a sign for Scotland which had just got her first parliament for three hunner year. We envisaged ye as wan o a new generation o Scots born intae a country that would eventually win her freedom and become a nation true tae hersel. We were, and still are, idealists. When ye turnt oot tae be the millennium babbie and put Scotland on the map, well, that appeared an even greater sign. We had sich hope, sich dreams for you, but we realised, or at least your faither did, that you could richt speedily become the victim of exploitation, so we turnt doon sponsorship, tried to gie you a normal life. Ah ken you've taen that ill sometimes.

Your faither and me parted soon efter the birth. We both kent that he could dae far mair guid for Scotland if his life wis no tainted by scandal. He does love ye Callie, it's just, we felt it was for the best, for oor nation.

Ah ken we've no seen eye tae eye on some things but whit mither an dochter dae, and ah hope ye've forgien me. We've aye had high hopes for ye, Callie, that ye'd mak somethin o yersel for Scotland.

Afore ye were born ah dreamed ye'd be somethin in the Parlia-
ment, the first President mibbe, but ah'm yer mither first and
foremost and ah want ye tae be happy and fulfilled, so ah'm prood
and pleased at the way ye're gaun on at the art school and ah've
nae doots ye'll be a fine artist fur Scotland wan o these days. Keep
faith in yersel and Scotland, lass.

Mither

* * *

Interview in *Lifestyle Magazine*, supplement of *The Sunday Scot* Newspaper
12.1.28

Caledonia Scott is a stunner. There's no other word for it. Graceful, elegant in understated designer clothing in neutral tones highlighted by her trademark tartan motif (this time on a wristwatch), she epitomises the successful young dynamic Scots businesswoman. I met her in the airy lounge of the Caledonia Hotel, and while she sipped mineral water and toyed delicately with an espresso, we discussed her life and work.

Fawn Jessop: Caledonia, can you tell me something about your latest collection. How does it develop themes from your previous ones?

CS: Well, Fawn, as you know, I've always specialised in quality clothing which is both wearable and elegant; good fabrics, easy lines but with that attention to detail which is so important. This season we're focusing on soft grey, fluidity, trouser suits especially. But modern women want something more; they want a touch of wit, irony even, which they find in my trademark tartan motif. Last season it was little faux-heatherspray brooches on the lapels; this season, as you can see, I'm concentrating on tartan watches, which are being made under special licence in collaboration with Schloss-S watches of Switzerland.

FJ: Yes I see you're wearing one now, and I can tell our readers it's a must-have for this season. But Caledonia, to get back to your work. You've been a runaway success over the past few years, both here and abroad, you've had award after award heaped on you, you have made your fortune. I know that in the past you haven't been too happy about talking about your background, and of course I don't wish to pry into your personal affairs, but after all, to some extent you've been in the limelight all your life. Do you think you've finally shaken off the tag 'Millennium Baby' or does it still haunt you?

CS: I like to think that I've now transcended it. I feel that's the best way to express it. It's true that when I was younger it was a bit of a millstone round my neck but now I've achieved success in my own right, well it's just part of me, not the whole.

FJ: What do you think of the current climate in Scotland for young businesspeople like yourself?

CS: It's the best ever. While I was studying it was still difficult to find markets, get capital, but since we became a fully federated member state of the Euro-American Alliance in 2021 things have really taken off.

FJ: So you don't agree with those political commentators who feel that the dream of total independence within Europe has been sold out?

CS: Not at all. What's the point of independence in the world we live in? Global markets are what's important. You can't get access to the kind of capital you need if you're a small nation. I mean we still have our identity. I'm sure part of the popularity of my work is because it's recognisably Scottish. Without the tartan motif it could be from any sophisticated European nation.

FJ: Of course. But what about other aspects of Scottish culture. Do you share the fears of those who worry about the effect of globalisation on national identity? Your own mother, of course, is untiring in her efforts to preserve and promote the Scots language, though many feel that it's now a dying battle.

CS: Of course I have the utmost respect for my mother's campaign, but I have to agree to differ from her. The Scots language is very important in the literature of Scotland and it's good to be able to appreciate Burns and Henryson, for example. But nowadays these are minority interests, really, best left to scholars. Of course there's a place for these kind of gatherings my mother organises where enthusiasts go to talk in Scots for the evening, but the kind of wholesale speaking and writing in Scots which she envisages, well, let's face it, it just won't happen anymore.

FJ: Yet I believe you did speak Scots yourself as a child.

CS: With respect, I've come a long way since then.

FJ: Though you do use Scots words in your collections, there was the mohair wrap from last winter you called the 'Coorie-in', wasn't there?

CS: Yes and you might remember the 'Thrawn Bag', which had a texture of thistles on its surface. But that's just the point I'm making. These are post-modern, post-millennium if you like; witty, ironic. My new collection of raincoats will be marketed under the name of 'A Smirr of Scotland'.

FJ: Well, Caledonia, thank you so much for your time. I'm sure that with people like you at the forefront of Scotland's business world the future of Caledonia is bright!

PETER DORWARD

The Remains

Did Pre-Ceramic Orkadians Have Access to Smelted Metal Alloys?

Prof. Humbert Plotnick; Dr Steven Allwyn; Dr Isabel Macloud
Dept. Archaeology and Paleo-Anthropology.
Christ's College, London
Correspondence: Prof. Plotnick

ABSTRACT

A preliminary qualitative analysis of spec. 253/c/ii (Cat. 17b), a high quality and near intact acid mulch preserved specimen of pre-ceramic *Homo Sapiens Orkadiensis*,[1] exhibiting prima facie evidence of precocious[2] metal implement contact or use. The authors examine the case for re-assessing our understanding of late Palaeolithic Orkadian technology[3] and trading relationships.[4]

INTRODUCTION

Within the overall context of Meso-Nordic migration[5] and settlement patterns in the late Palaeolithic, attention focuses inevitably on the case of the pre-ceramic communities,[6] the so called Limpet Eaters of Hafström[7], in the northern Orkadian archipelago.

But it wasn't Issie that found him – it was me.

She's skittering around in the mud and then she's on her arse. I'm running up behind, chasing her, shouting tear-blinded at this yellow waterproof back, but admiring too, with a colder part of me, how this lassie can sit there in the wet peat cursing like a tinker and yet still slay me.

'Wait Issie! Wait fir me! Please wait!' In my own ears my voice sounds like a bairn's. Breathless – too many fags – I skitter down the incline myself and land on *my* arse beside her.

But I've fuck all to say when I get there.

'Jist wanted tae talk,' I say, weakly. 'Ah jist really wanted tae talk.'

Little boy voice of mine, whining like a whelp. I plead too easily, least that's what my mother always used to say, no pride, and now something's got stuck for good, for I find now persuading's hard and when I try it, I whine.

Issie white and a wee bit breathless, she puts her head in her hands, says

'Fuck fuck fuck . . .'

I put my arm around her shoulder, squeeze too tight, my poor wee voice cracking again.

'Issie!'

And she shakes herself free of my grip, angry, shaking herself dry of me like my dog might do, and says,

'Leave me alone Robbie! Please! I just wanted a moment! I just need to *think*!'

My eyes say clear that I don't understand, and now there's tears in her's too.

'We're *leaving* tomorrow! I'm going!'

She sobs. But I say nothing. I just stare.

'There's nothing I can do about it! Do you understand? I'm leaving!'

I just stare at the ground, where the rain falls in a pool in a peat-hole I must have cut same time last year when everything was different, and I see something there: the glint of bright metal where there should be no metal: this shape taking form in the mud.

'I just wish now I'd never come. I'm sorry Robbie . . .'

Then Issie sees it too. Stops her crying flat. Wipes her nose on her sleeve and sniffs. Knows in an instant what we're looking at.

She's quiet now. Jumps down, sinks to her knees in peat. She half crawls over, bends down, touches it with a finger, wipes away the mud, exposes the black leather skin of its hand, the metal still grasped there, and snatches her own hand away as if she's touched or taken a thing she shouldn't have.

'Robbie,' she says, quiet now and the colour of her voice quite changed, 'wait here, hmm? Just don't move. Don't touch it, I'll be right back.'

And she left me alone with it.

CONTEXT AND TOPOGRAPHY

Hafström (*see map fig. 1*) is an isolated, trackless and uninhabited islet, 8km long and 3km wide at its widest point, lying in open sea 15km north east of the main Orkadian archipelago. It is now given over primarily to the seasonal grazing of sheep, and some artesanal harvesting by mainland fishermen of the extensive mussel beds off the north coast.

The central topography consists of a flat-topped hillock (*Suilven Beag, map fig. 2*) backed by broken ground to the southern cliffs, and extensive primary peat marshland extending to the sand-beaches of the northern and western littorals.

The main loci of excavation (*OS 674239; 673236; April–October 1998*) centered on Palaeolithic midden heaps just north of the mainly ruined farmstead *Tigh Ander*, and the sight of a chance find some 1.2km to the south east.

They don't knock or anything, just walk in my door. I'm making fire, boiling water for my dinner. I note the barking of the dog, turn round and they're all standing at my shoulders gouping like I was a spirit, and me as frighted to see them too.

'Who are you?'

The oldest of my three guests. Face like a billie-goat: bald head, specs on a brightly coloured cord so he doesn't lose them, boots, waterproof, speaks American, his head thrust forward like a snake, spitting words. Always grieved about some thing. Some cunt aye pissing on his strawberries. Bert. *Humbert.*

'Live here. Who the fuck 'r you?'

'You *live* here?'

As if I'm just a speck of shite. Different voice. Steven the Englishman. Then an apologetic smile, gives me an encouraging, friendly sort of nod. That's his manner: contempt followed by the cover up. Steven, who lies, gets lied to. I nod.

'Alone?'

Good looking boy, Stevie, though he wears blue specs, now all spattered with rain, like weather on a windscreen.

'Til *you* came, aye, shite breath.'

A little tinkling laugh and shite breath looks perplexed. Issie.

'Who is it Steven?'

She emerges from behind them, sees me, stops, stares, mouth open. Almost as if she knows me already. Almost as if we've known one another for years.

'Pardon ma French. Didnae ken ther wis a lassie tae.'

Issie: skin the colour of dark sand on the beach; long, black, curling hair; slate-blue eyes; a curious smile; a laugh like bird song after a long, dark winter.

'This is Doctor Macloud,' says blue specs putting an arm around Issie's shoulders. Issie not too keen on this, I see, from the shrinking in her eye. 'Doctor Plotnick.' Nods at Goat Head, who nods back. 'Steven Allwyn.' Holds out a hand to shake. I look at it, look at Issie, who smiles at me then for the first time, the first smile ever.

'Come on in then,' I say, for Issie's look has changed something for me; her smile has altered in an instant the weave and colour of things.

'Keep the cold oot. There'll be food presently. Ah dinnae get much company.'

And the three duck their heads to mind the hanging tallow-light; they let the winnock swing back, walk in to this one small place left here where it's still cosy warm, where the peat fire still burns and smokes all the nicht and there's a rabbit boiling on the stove.

Although the site has been greatly disrupted, presumably through the activities of mainland migrant shepherds, the topography of the *Tigh Ander* site is clear even on a cursory inspection. A central enclosure of early Orkadian Dolmus[10] structure is surrounded by a number of stone built livestock enclosures, mostly roofless and dilapidated, one showing evidence of more recent inhabitation.

The whole is surrounded and partially buried by a typical crustacean shell, bone and animal faeces insulating midden.

A random 'meter quadrant' survey of the midden yielded the following (anticipated) constituents:

Sea shell: 14.2% (Mussel; limpet; crab; unidentified)
Bone: 7% (Gull; Puffin; Rabbit; Ovine; Human)
Faeces: 18.7% (Rabbit; Ovine; Canine; Human).

Like bairns playing at chuckie stains. The one stood and threw this brightly coloured square backwards over his shoulder, the others found where it landed and marked the spot. They argued, then started to dig with little shovels, shoveled all the shite they dug up into wee plastic bags which Goat Head then sealed with sticky tape and put a label on. If I'd kent the shite round here was so precious I'd have bagged it up mesel'.

For days after they came, I felt heavy in my heart. On my tod too long, the presence of these three outsiders weighed. I couldn't sleep. In the dark I heard them move around, re-arranging their stuff, the scratch of their pencils as they took their notes, the chink of their wee shovels and pick heads, the grunting of the old one as he stood outside trying so hard to pish.

I heard them whispering at night. I heard the old man muttering to the younger, and I heard the younger mutter sharply back. I heard Issie turning in her sleep, and even from where I lay on the other side of the curtain, felt the warmth of her sleeping, heard the murmuring of her night breathing, and wished that she was gone.

So I stood awhile that day watching them play their games, but soon grew tired of it, called the dog and took a walk to check the traps. I crossed the brow of the hill, found two fat does caught in the wires and the one not yet dead. I killed it with gralloching hook and gave the blood and gralochings to the dog who looked at me with a dog smile on her slavering chops and for an instant warmed me.

In the mornings I like to sit a while where it's sheltered, between the jaws of rock which make the north bay, to contemplate the sea, to breakfast on the shellfish I find there at my feet. I dream. At the time of year when the weather's light and the sky clear and a man can see a long way yonder over the sea, I watch the black shapes of birds fishing, half hidden by the sighing of the waves; watch waves cutting the water and think them the dark sails of boats with people coming; I see the white beards of waves and I think about spears and arrows and men clad in sea-drenched leather running and shouting on the beach. I'm a richt dreamer, or so my mother used to say, though it was she that told me all these stories first.

There was someone watching me.

My dog was sleeping at my feet. With the lang-nail on my right thumb I prised open another mussel shell, supped out the broth and the meat.

I heard her coming down the bank behind me. The dog pricked up her ears, and I put a hand on her shoulders to quiet him. She sat beside me, looked a while at the little pile of shells at my feet, said

'Who *are* you Robbie?'

. . . reveals three distinct stages of settlement, each with characteristic midden strata:

1. The Limpet Eaters. Mid-late Palaeolithic, almost certainly representing the first Meso-Nordic fixed settlements, subsisting entirely on artesanal fishing and trapping,[13] and with practically no evidence of contact with Scandinavian or Pictish influence, and lacking metal implements or ceramics.

2. Meso-Nordic. Early Viking trading kinships, which seem, by absorption or conquest to have entirely supplanted the pre-existing settlers,[14] formed transient settlements themselves, and developed sophisticated trading relationships and the use of metal tools, and the ability to work precious and semi-precious metals.

3. Early modern-contemporary. There is evidence of settlement by seasonal shepherds and fisherman up until the middle years of this century.

Preliminary work suggests that spec. 253/c/ii represents the liminal interface of stages of 1. and 2.

What could I say Issie? What could I tell you?

I can remember a busier time. I can remember Faither, and his two brothers, and there was an old, old woman whom we all cried Grannie who told my sister and me long tales in the night by the peat fire. I can remember too when Faither died, when my uncle drowned, and I remember when Mother died, of course, and that even wasn't too long since. That left my sister, Agnes, and me, but Agnes went so, so sad when all the rest were dead that she left for the mainland, to be with other folk, and I've never seen *her* since either. Which left just me and the dog and her whelp, and then the dog died, which left the whelp which is my dog now, and when she dies I'll away to the mainland and find myself another, because I don't wish ever to be left alone.

Issie listened to me. I looked out on the long sea as I talked, as I told this to another for the first ever time, and it wasn't the wind in my eye but a tear which blurred me.

'And you never leave?'

To the mainland twice a year when I work on the boats, buy fags and books and come back again.

I'm a private man: unused to talking at all with others; and Issie knew that and understood it for she talked gently about this thing or that thing and never rushed at a thing too directly.

Issie put her hand over mine as we talked, and soon I had mine on hers, the lang-nail of my thumb stroking her smooth skin and the thing, the talking, became a habit.

She opened me like a mussel; supped my broth, took the meat and swallowed me, left my empty shell.

Spec. 253/c/ii was identified by chance during the tenth and final week of the primary investigation. Lying in partly eroded acid mulch peat, which had served to protect the specimen and maintain it in almost perfect preservation, the integrity of the site had become compromised by natural weathering processes, which, although enabling the find, also made necessary the emergency excavation and removal of the specimen to a secure place. Despite our best efforts the cadaver sustained some minor damage prior to and during excavation.

'Robbie, I told you not to touch it!'

But I found it. In a sense, it was mine.

I could see what had once been its face; its eye lids as fine and wrinkled as black purse leather; mouth pulled away to one side leering at the sky like a flatfish. With hooked finger I pulled more mud from the soft cavity of its mouth. I touched the soft hair; and what had once been its red hair, weakened so much by so many years, broke in my hands.

'For Christ's, don't touch it!'

Steven jumped down, cowped in the mud beside me, got a faceful of peat and shite and lost his specs. He grabbed me by the shoulders, tried to pull me away, so I turned and skelped him with my lang-nail, laid open Stevie's smooth face which maddened him, and in no time at all we're both of us lying in the peat-mud fighting, coiled together tight like two sand worms.

Issie shouted, and we stopped, and she let herself down again beside us, looking with a black face at two boys that hated one another, and pretending she didn't know why.

On her haunches, staring, air whistling through her nose.

The remains of some fabric was still on its shoulder, stained deep brown and spoiled like the rest of it, but once precious. Clothes which once belonged; which were once warmed by the heat from its body.

The arm stretched out above the head, saluting, the face half buried in the armpit, the hand fisted. The long, sharp thumb nail, still unbroken, the lang-nail.

Issie stared awhile at the now empty fist. She stared back up at me, eyes asking, but nothing said, and I just stared back, as if I didn't know, or didn't understand.

The disposition of spec. 253/c/ii gives an unmistakable impression of flight (*Fig. iii*). The figure lay headlong in acid peat, face down, head and outstretched arm directed away from the dolmus settlement. The right arm was stretched out to its full extent above the head, the right hand formed into a fist, whilst the left hand and arm partly protected the face. The head was turned slightly to the left, as if the specimen were looking half over his shoulder at the moment he fell.

At the time of death, the figure was lightly clad in a woven tunic of material as yet unidentified (*Table iv*), goat skin breeches and shoes stitched with flax, a girdle, and a small purse of goat skin containing a number of gull-bone fish hooks.

There was some evidence of disturbance to the site, possibly the result of bird activity just prior to excavation, which inevitably obscures attempts to interpret the circumstances surrounding the subject's death.

It is tempting nonetheless to ask the question: what precipitated the subject's flight? From whom, or what, did he attempt to escape?

'I'm a palao-anthropologist Robbie. Do you know what that means?'

I nodded, but didn't really.

'It means I've spent my life looking at the bits and bones of people that have been dead for thousands of years, trying to put together a picture of who they were and what they were like. How they would have thought. How they felt. The sorts of things they would have said.'

We walked a lot during those first weeks. I taught her the place. I showed her where Faither and his brother kept the boat before the boat was lost; where we collected bones for hooks; the best place to set a night line for mackerel and dog fish; the place on the headline where there once stood standing stones, thrown down a hundred years since, but still there, reclining in flat circles, and still a place to visit on a wild night. And I showed her the quiet places too: where we buried my drowned uncle; the stones marking Maither and Faither; the cave where I played with Agnes; and all the other quiet places, all the places where you hear the winds and water whisper; all those places still woven in the spoiled fabric of my memory.

'But it's more than curiosity Robbie. It's a passion too. I love this wild island as much as you do: maybe more, because I come from outside and see it differently.'

'But you'll leave.'

She just nodded. She ran her hand over the skin of my back, and the sand trapped between our skins made her smooth touch rough.

'I'll miss this place.'

'But you'll take the memory with you.'

A wave crossed the mouth of the cave, broke on the sand bar, sent a film of sea-spit to the dry sand where we lay.

'We'd better be going. Tide's coming up.'

Issie stood, brushed the sand from her skin, turned her back to me, blocking the light coming in the mouth of the cave. She was watching the red sun sink over the curved sea. She turned to me after a moment, but I couldn't see her face, only the red sun shining, framed in the cave mouth, picking out the filaments of her hair. The rest was in shadow.

. . . clean shaven male in his made to late thirties, ~192Cm, ~71Kg, Body Mass Index 21.4Cm/M^2, of somewhat endomorphic habitus, the skin, subcutaneous fat and internal organs well preserved by acid saponification. A generally worn dentition, absence of any degree of carious attack, together with evidence of early osteoarthrosis affecting both hips and lumbosacral spine, and an old, well united fracture of the mid-shaft of the humerus, are all typical findings in specimens of hunter-gatherers, or limpet eaters, of this period.

Cause of death was, given a specimen of this age, remarkably clear. An intricately worked bronze alloy arrow-head of typically Meso-Nordic design was found deeply embedded in the space between cervical vertebraes 3 and 4, cleanly transecting the spinal cord at this level. The remains of the shaft were of yew, a wood never indigenous to this part of the Orkadian archipelago, and the point of entry of the missile just caudal to the nape of the neck. The presence of peat mulch in the upper airways, and below the level of the larynx would suggest the proximate cause of death to be asphyxiation. The specimen would have lain, effectively paralysed, for some hours before death.

The extremely sophisticated workmanship of the arrow-head suggests to the authors, following the work of *Zembla et al*, a purpose beyond the merely cotidian: such pieces were used more typically for sport, or ceremony, than the simple collection of food.

'I *will* leave,' she said, after her moment of staring. 'In a month or so, when the work's done, and the weather changes. I'll go back to my world, and you'll stay here in yours, won't you?'

I nodded. I supposed that what she said was true.

'But I'll not forget you Robbie. That's the point: I'll not forget this time.'

'It's getting late.'

We walked back together across the island. Content, we shared our silence. We walked slowly, and by the time we were home it was night.

*   *   *

'Doctor Macloud has stated to us that there was a metal object gripped in the first, and now it is gone. We *have* to find out what happened to it.'

Issie has a different face on her now, though. Just one month passed, and she looks down at me angry, like the mother of a bad child.

They're all gathered there. Steven, pleased to be on Issie's right side once again; Plotnick, who is speaking, head thrust forward, tongue flicking between thin lips. Outside, wrapped in plastic, canvass, tarpaulin and tied tight in a parcel with string, the silent fourth, wrenched at last from his hole, bound up and ready to be taken away. My guests have all turned against me. The dog whines and growls. I say nothing.

Now Issie begs.

'Robbie, this is *theft!* It's a criminal offence to steal from a dig!'

Embarrassed, she looks to her friends, appealing, then leans forward, feigns a kind of lost intimacy.

'Robbie, don't you see, it would have made no difference . . .' – then the lie – 'I would have come back anyway . . .' Steven turns his head away, his fine face now a study in embarrassment and contempt.

But still she doesn't understand, and so I hold my silence.

Tense, Steven wipes his specs.

'Robbie, you have to understand how important this is. We can't finish our work . . .'

Suddenly Plotnick rages.

'Which is exactly what this . . . *caveman* . . . wants!'

He stands, waving his shovel in his hand, shouting.

'If our host sees fit to steal, then we must simply retrieve what is our property . . .' Goat Head steps forward to where I sit hunched in my silence, he raises his hand to me, and the dog, my quiet dog, grips his flesh in her teeth, and the old man howls.

'Call your dog off!' shouts Steven, the arse enraged at the liberties I permit my pet, then sets about my whining dog with the blunt edge of a pick.

Plotnick, silent, winds a hankie round his bleeding wrist. Steven stands, breathless, angry, shamed, staring at me. The dog lies dead. Issie sobs.

'Why wouldn't you just tell us where it is . . .?'

Notwithstanding the considerable uncertainty which shrouds the case, the circumstances surrounding the death of spec. 253/c/ii provide clear, and dramatic, if not unambiguous evidence, of an hitherto unrecognised access to smelted bronze weaponry, by the limpet eating communities of Hafström.

It is established beyond doubt, following *Plotnick et al (1987)* that limpet eaters themselves lacked the technological capacity to smelt and work metal, implying therefore a trading, or more bellicose relationship, with either the proto *p*-Celtic kingdom to the south, or the Meso-Nordic kinships to the north. The quality and style of workmanship of the missile which ended the life of spec. 253/c/ii would suggest the latter.

Little is known about the end of the Limpet Eating communities of Hafström. Whether the communities died out through emigration to the richer, less harsh lands to the south, or whether still viable communities were absorbed by the waves of Meso-Nordic migration which occurred in the mid-late Palaeolithic, or were simply exterminated, is the subject of intense speculation in the academy.[26] Clearly the answers to the above questions depend not simply on the circumstances of the life and death of spec. 253/c/ii, but also on those of the person who fired the arrow which killed him: information which, sadly, will never now be known.

This is how it would have been.

An act of theft, to simply own a precious thing. Or to reclaim an object, which had first belonged to the thief, and been taken unfairly from him. Or the thing stolen as bait to keep the lover still with him, or to make her return. Or stolen to spite the lover who had spited him.

A woman's amulet made of highly worked gold, still bright, untarnished despite its age and years in the ground, carved with shapes or letters cut with some sharp tool into its substance. The thing too small to fit around the thief's wrist, he carries it wrapped tight in his right hand as he runs.

There is no where for him to go. The scent of burning in his nose, the shouts and laughter of his pursuers, the hammering of his heart in his chest as he runs.

Or perhaps they left the thing there for him, in order that he *should* steal it; in order that they might pursue him . . .

He would have run to the top of a gentle slope, stopped there, realising that there was nothing more than marshland between him and the beach, and beyond the beach, the sea; that he might run and run, but that eventually he would be caught.

And so he half turns his head, to see how close they are. He sees them standing, catching their breath, a hundred, two hundred yards away, laughing, whilst the younger and bravest of them points his finger, draws a bright arrow, strings his bow.

*   *   *

There were no more words said. The weather was turning and they were running out of time. I helped them carry their things down to the beach. There was barely space enough in the launch – for their bags, themselves, the samples, the dead man, wrapped up and stolen from his grave.

They muttered instructions to one another, climbed aboard, pulled twice on the engine cord before it started, and guided the prow slowly between the rocks of the north bay. Issie looked at me just once – a glance from a bland, open face; neither shame, regret nor anger written on it – then she turned her head away.

This is how it would have been.

I have a young woman's gold amulet gripped tightly in the fist of my right hand. My right arm is stretched out above my head, the left bent across my face. This is how I fell: glancing over my left shoulder, my head bent sharply back, my right cheek forced into my under arm.

Above my left shoulder I can see clouds gather in a heavy sky. Two gulls land on the heather bank above me, hop from webbed foot to webbed foot, calling to one another, hoping for my eyes.

My face sinks slowly into mud. It becomes harder and harder to breath.

DAVID EDWARDS

The Sick Man of Europe

I get up at five on Monday bin day. I'll have a breakfast of
porridge and tea. The old kettle is pre-1960 and takes an age
to boil. While it boils I'll roll a couple of roll-ups from the
tobacco tin – my own blend, hand-picked from hundreds of
quality butt ends. I always have an eye for a good butt.

Last Monday it was a shaping up to be a scorcher, a
beautiful morning. From my window at the top of the flats I
can watch the sun rising over the port. I was sitting enjoying
the view, then mother pops into my head and I remember
how she used to potter around in the kitchen of a morning in
one of those funny pink flowered aprons and hair-net. She
hoped I would buy the flat off of the council when I got back
from the Navy. But I went and followed Billy around.
Endless parties on Easter Road. Drugs and bands. Only
ended up blowing the lot. He kind of dropped me, stopped
phoning and that, when my thinning hair made a fucking
mockery of a feather cut. Back in the seventies hair mattered
more. He had a thick black mane, like that guy from The
Free. Still see him, married, lives with his ex-wife down Leith
– took to the drink, big-time. Ma loved that guy. If I'd
bought the hoose it wouldn't make a difference anyway.

I fancied cheese toast that day. I'd found a 10lb cake of Edam cheese outside the deli in Marchmont on Sunday morning and a large sack of lentils. Slightly out of date but it looked nobad to me. As I cut off a wedge I remembered that arse at the chippy the night before. When I asked for a half poke of chips, the wanker laughed and jabbered something in Italian to his fat mother. She giggled away over the white-pudding fucking supper she was wrapping. I'm no' having that, I thought, so I got him to specially rip the the paper poke right down the side and spread the sauce all over the chips, not just the top. Cos your chips are shite, I said under my breath as I left the shop. I was a a wee bit pissed that day – giro day.

I felt like a wee nip that morning after the cheese toast. I got the rig tied to the bike rack and pumped up the tyres, put on my boiler suit and ended off. I started the bucket raking about five years past. All my home entertainment has come from the buckets. Tam and I have rigged up a pretty smart computer rig from parts I've picked up. Tam's trying to tap into government computers, says we'll make a mint from some kind of fraud. I'm no into that stuff. The Internet would do me, just for the info on gardening, things that interest me. Ken's away with the goaly anyway. We've rigged up the net, gives me direct access to those high heedyens at the council, like councillor Graham. Save me cycling all the way to the office for which, I may add, I am not reimbursed on the mileage like that arse. Fixing up a mini system just now, all it needs is a few fuses. I'll sell the old one.

I started my bucket round down the bottom of Oxgangs. Usual crap, though it's surprising you get some of the best stuff from the schemes – thats where I got the Amstrad. Nothing like that, but I picked up an old steel wheely trolley I could use as a free-standing pot holder down at the allotment, maybe, strapped it on anyway. I make a wide circle round the benefits office and did the deli and restaurants in Morningside. Got a bag of yesterday's filled rolls. Do me a week. By the way, I never usually tell anyone what I get cos it's my personal business. That's sensible round this area. I have to stick to the side streets now, with those fucking wheely-bins, they've made the work a lot harder.

By the time I got to the back end of Princes Street it was scorching. Suited figures start to appear as the first few buses of the day push out the flocks of seagulls chattering and bickering over over last night's burger trays. I think to myself how Scotland doesn't suit the heat – only grates against the tedium of the day and ferments the dregs of years of fustration. Which is one reason I have to hurry back; to avoid the packs of schemies who are drawn to the town in such weather. I am not unaware of how eccentric I look.

I make it home, back to Nelson Mandela flats, for 11 a.m. Early enough to avoid trouble.

I'm not stupid, I've thought about all this stuff. Thought about one possible reason for this garbage obsession. A reason apart from the fact that of course, I'm continually skint. I mind when I was a lad I used to tip the rubbish for mother. Out in the stair there was a steel hatch that when you pushed its top the bottom would swing open. When you opened it it would create a breezy echo that came from the long rubbish shoot running the length of the building. A peculair, sweetish smell of rubbish hit you then. I liked that smell. I would get a thrill from stuffing our bag of rubbish in the hatch and listening to it clunk its way down the steel chute. It was like I could feel that bag falling, gathering velocity for its final, crunching thud. I would often stand there for an hour or so playing with the chute. I could hardly hear Ma's sobs as Pa belted her when he came back from the pub. I'd slink back in to my wee room when the noise had died down. That went on for years. If I stayed out of the way I'd avoid a serious beating. Pa was a big, thick-set man with a black tash. He always slobbed around the house in a simit vest and trousers, a big old bastard. By the time I was sixteen I'd had more than enough so when the chance to join the merchant navy came up at the annual careers talk I took it.

You can view the children's playground from the flat. Hear them shouting and squealing their heads off. I'll take a drink after a bucket round, sit at the table fixing the Akai midi system, half watching the children, half concentrating on the wires and fuses. I'll stop every now and then to roll a fag from the special blend. They were good days on the ships. Got away from this place and mother. This place, I could never be what I really am in this place. Fucking incredible days. I'm a bit of an old-fashioned sort of sailor, if you ken what I mean. I would skirt around the issue here, but it wasn't long before I found my stride on the boats. Hundreds of great shags in every port, no bother. Days drenched in the sun. The Berlin Sauna scene in the seventies was something else, those queens were fucking amazing as long as you avoided the inevitable cat fights. And of course everyone loved a sailor then and I looked the business. I cannae be the same here. I've only got the porn on the net next door. Crap stuff. I'll cycle past those graveyards at night, but I never go in, they hard looking youths give me the shits. I took a rent once, when I was desperate but the whole thing was so sad it depressed me. Anyway, those kind of days are over for me. It's only when I've had a skinful that the terrible longing returns.

In the afternoon I'll go down to the allotment. It's a special place, the allotment. It's where I do the real work. Tatties, leeks, carrots, lettuce, a large compost bin and toms in the shed, on a warm summer's afternoon you can't beat it. The sun illuminates all my work. I can feel it all growing. I like the feel of the soil in the grains of my palms and between my fingers. There's a nice little community of folks down there, not much hassle. Vandals got the shed last year, the little bastards tore it apart. Why do they have to do that? I'll catch the fuckers one day. The allotment is the one decent thing father gave us.

When he died I was in the Azores. I got the call from Ma. I sat in the cabin and thought about it. It felt good then that he was gone, but as the days went on a kind home-sickness came over me and I knew I was going home. The sound of mother's endless sobbing got to me, though why she mourned for that animal I don't know. Well I do, one of those loyalty things or maybe crying for herself. It all reminded me of that chute and I knew it was time to feel that fucking Scottish gravity again. I knew it would be the death of me.

I got this leaflet from the dole the other day all about good eating habits, giving up smoking and cutting back on drinking. The first thing I thought was how much it must have cost them to send out and what gave an overpaid suit the right to tell me what to do. I have the healthiest fucking lifestyle going, organic food, plenty of exercise and no stress-packed holidays in the sun and most of all, no fucking family, job and mortgage. I'm not giving into the social planners. What they want is to create nice, managable little work units. Do this, don't do that. You have to get out of the place to realise just how fucking controlled we are in this little country. Someone must be winning somewhere. Not that I'm jealous, as long as they just leave me alone. But the truth is that I don't own or control anything in my life. Is this an advantage or not? I suppose I'll never really know.

This will be the last bucket round. The part-time worker at the benefits office has given me full and final notice that disability benefit will be terminated due to a tightening of the criteria. I'll be lined up with some kind of menial work, such as basket-making or stacking shelves at the supermarket. That's what it all seems to add up to in this place – alpha, beta and delta work units primed for work on foriegn investment projects or servants for our expanding tourist market.

The high flats offer a perfect suicide opportunity so long as the wind drives in a northerly direction. I think I'll go with the boiler suit on, less chance of losing limbs across the street on impact. Somewhere I may get a mention but I doubt it, can't see what kind of agenda I would assist. Just hope I'm out of it when it comes to that final thud.

I hope for a single moment of clarity on that final fall. A moment of condensed time where I can just about be me. Not to feel the constant nagging of the past would be such a relief. The only regret is that I'll be leaving the allotment to the those arses at the council. But why not, they'll be the ones that have to deal with the funeral and everything. Truly, the public authority have provided from cradle to grave. I have left instructions in the hut relating to planting and crop rotation. I'm sure the whole episode will create quite a stir down there. I don't want to upset anyone, it's just that the time is right. But some lucky person will inherit a brilliant plot.

DAVID EWEN

God's Breath

It rose from the ground and shimmied upwards, propelled by a lungful of energy, its lazy tail strung out behind. At the top of the fast hard climb it suddenly stalled and peeled off into a dive, swinging upwards again in an attenuated arc. Twenty, thirty times it swooped before becoming scrappy in its movements.

Eighty feet below Father Irvine felt the rope tighten about his hands. His wheelchair rocked against its brake, tilting sideways, before the rope slipped from his grasp, burning his flesh as it did so.

From behind the garden wall Sister Arlyn saw the crazy scything in the sky. She dropped her secateurs and ran towards the gate. Father Irvine was still in his wheelchair when she arrived, his head bowed towards his abraded palms. He turned towards the young nun panting at his side. 'Looks like I'm going to need a new kite,' he said with a smile.

Dinner was always served at 7 p.m. The fourteen nuns were all meat-eaters which made cooking much easier. Tonight they were having beef stew and dumplings. Sister Lindsey, the Mother Superior, spooned two dollops onto each plate and passed it along the table. The conversation was terse and functional and overshadowed by the chunky rain slapping against the convent window. Suddenly there was a new, frightening sound in the hall: a knife dancing on the floor at the feet of Father Irvine.

'Are your hands still sore?' said Sister Lindsey, unfazed.

'No, I'm just a little tired,' said Father Irvine.

'A fresh knife, Sister Arlyn.'

The young nun rose from her seat and fetched the piece of cutlery, laying it before Father Irvine whom she was seated next to. The rest of the nuns resumed eating.

'Will you still be fit to go into town next Thursday?' said Sister Lindsey.

'I've told you – I don't want to see any more doctors,' said the elderly monk.

'I thought you might like to vote.'

'For what?'

'For your parliament,' she said wearily.

'Did you know that the parliament building was designed by a Spaniard?' said Father Irvine, picking up his knife with a bandaged hand. 'It's based on an upturned boat. An upturned boat . . .' He shook his head and pushed a dumpling onto his fork.

'Perhaps it's a symbol of a fearless, hard-working nation,' said Sister Lindsey.

'Or one cut adrift and due to sink.'

One of the younger nuns laughed and immediately regretted it. The Mother Superior stared at her for a second before turning back towards Father Irvine. 'Scotland would be better off on its own,' she said.

'So would Grampian,' said the monk. 'We produce one quarter of the country's food, most of its fish, we have reasonable claim to its oil.'

Sister Lindsey was unsure how to reply. She was about to say something when Father Irvine started coughing violently. 'Quickly!' she shouted at Sister Arlyn, 'we need to get him to his room.'

Father Irvine lay on the bed, curled upon himself like a baby bird. His body was pallid and degraded expect for the bulbous nose which hung like a drip from his face. Sometimes Sister Arlyn imagined he was melting, draining away like a snowman. She would laugh at the thought until she remembered he was dying from lung cancer.

'Do you want some water?' she said when he finally stirred. The monk looked at her questioningly. 'You collapsed. It's two in the morning.' Father Irvine coughed again, gently this time, stifling the sound with his hand. As he took it away he noticed two neat globules of blood on the bandage, joined by a string of pinkish saliva. He closed his eyes again and lent back against his pillow.

'*Help me, please . . .*'

Father Irvine stared up at Jesus. The two men either side of him were dead, their mouths and eyes packed with the fine red dust which reeled around the crosses like phantom dancers. In the distance he could hear jackdaws, cawing in the hills high above Calvary, impatient for the dawn.

'*Help me, please,*' *said Jesus.*

By morning the rain had stopped. Snow lay like mildew across the mountains. There were few jagged peaks, few ostensible dangers, but looking towards the sprawling, cliff-bitten tundra, Sister Lindsey could appreciate the scale of the Cairngorms; the ease of getting lost in mist, the difficulty of escape. She turned away from the window and walked back towards her desk.

'We can't force him to go into hospital,' she said to Sister Arlyn who stood before her, hands clasped reverentially.

'But that's where he belongs,' protested the young nun.

'I agree but we have an obligation. Caring for the sick is something we've always done. The Sisters have looked after men from his order for hundreds of years.'

'He needs a nurse, a proper nurse.'

'He knows that.'

Sister Arlyn became distressed, 'So why doesn't he ask for one?' she said. 'Why doesn't he go into hospital?'

'Maybe he's in denial.' The Mother Superior sat down at her desk. 'I watched my father die in the same way; watched him cough himself inside-out. He kept working, kept joking, kept on as normal until the blood came. Then I watched him turn into a child, just like me . . . ten years old . . . clinging to life like it was some kind of favourite doll. It wasn't brave: it was a tantrum. He had nothing to hold onto in death because he had nothing to hold onto in life, only politics, God bless him.' She stood up and approached Sister Arlyn. 'Do you know why a newborn baby cries? Because its first breath burns. For most people the last one's no easier. When my father started whimpering, that's when I stopped. You've got to be strong Sister Arlyn. For Father Irvine.'

Father Irvine stood before Jesus, regarding his feet then his hands, then his feet again.

'Please, help me,' said Jesus.

The monk took a step backwards and started to undo the rope around his cassock, still staring at the crude iron pegs pinning Jesus to the cross. He let the garment fall into the dust and remained where he was, quite naked.

'What are you doing?'

Father Irvine was jolted from his reverie and found Sister Arlyn dragging his wheelchair backwards. 'You could have gone over the edge,' she said desperately.

'I'm sorry, I must have fallen asleep.'

'Why didn't you lock your wheels?'

'I thought I did. I couldn't have put the brake on properly. It's quite stiff. It needs some oil.'

Sister Arlyn swung him around and headed back towards the convent. 'You're lucky. I was just coming to get you for lunch.'

'What is for lunch?' he said calmly. Sister Arlyn was still angry and didn't reply. 'It's apple-pie for dessert, isn't it?'

'Yes,' she conceded. 'With raspberries.'

'Will you help me build a new kite?' he said without pause.

'I don't know anything about kites . . .'

'I'll tell you what to do. We just need materials – some twine, some glue, some polythene.'

'We don't have any polythene here.'

'We could even paint it.'

'I'd have to ask the Mother Superior.'

'She doesn't need to know.'

'She'll see you flying it.'

'We could paint her face on it. She could watch over us all.' Sister Arlyn suppressed a little smile.

At lunch a radio broadcast replaced the sound of the weather. The newsreader described a serious car crash involving two German tourists. There was some cheery news about plans to build a new sports stadium on the outskirts of Aberdeen and then an election update. The Nationalists were said to be trailing Labour by four points in the opinion polls.

'You can switch it off now,' said Sister Lindsey to an elderly nun. 'It looks like we'll need your vote, Father Irvine.'

'I meant what I said about independence for the region,' he said. 'Why should we share our wealth with the Central Belt when the Nationalists refuse to share Scotland's wealth with England?'

'Because we're all Scots, that's why.'

'I'm sorry but it means nothing to me. It's just a line on a map.'

'Have you got no sense of history?'

'Scotland has traditionally been at war with itself.'

'Not since the days of St Columba. "That man is little to be envied whose patriotism would not gain force upon the plain of Marathon, or whose piety would not grow warmer in the ruins of Iona." Dr Johnson's observation.'

'St Columba came from Ireland. He was a Gael, not a Pict.'

'He was a *Christian*,' said Sister Lindsey firmly.

That evening Sister Arlyn approached the Mother Superior about Father Irvine's desire to build a new kite. Sister Lindsey continued to light candles in the chapel as the young nun spoke.

'You mustn't encourage him,' said Sister Lindsey. 'You saw his hands.'

'He said they're healing.'

'An infection could kill him.'

'He's dying as it is,' said Sister Arlyn with mild irritation.

'I've told you, we're all dying. That's no reason to get hysterical.'

'It's only a kite.' Sister Lindsey stared at the young nun, taken aback by her dissent. 'He said he wants to feel God's breath,' continued Sister Arlyn.

'And what does that mean?'

'I think he just wants to be outside.'

'He can go outside. But no kite.'

When Sister Arlyn told Father Irvine this, he seemed distraught, inordinately so. She had waited a few days before doing so and chose a sunny afternoon in the garden, hoping the pleasant weather would detract from his disappointment. It didn't, yet he seemed reluctant to explain why.

'Do you think Jesus was a good carpenter?' he said. 'The Bible doesn't say much about his day job, does it?'

'You sound disrespectful,' said Sister Arlyn.

'Do you think it would be it was a family business. "Joseph and Son"?'

'It would be God and Son,' said Sister Arlyn, piqued by the danger of the conversation.

'That's really living in the shadow of your father, isn't it? God makes a man, Jesus makes a chair. Maybe that's why he started doing miracles; to get his old man's respect.'

Sister Arlyn composed herself. 'It's not God's fault you're ill,' she said.

'Yes it is. He made us mortal.'

'And Jesus offers us immortality.'

'I don't feel let down. I feel like I've let Jesus down.'

Father Irvine proceeded to describe a recurring dream. He could offer no elucidation but admitted it left him feeling guilty. In his dream he came upon Jesus after his crucifixion. Rather than rescuing him, he tied his cassock to the cross and flew it like a kite, using his belt to control it.

'Jesus was terrified at first but then he started to relax and enjoy himself,' he said. 'He forgot about his fear and the pain in his hands and feet.' Father Irvine smiled but became solemn. 'And then the wind changed direction and he got tangled up in a tree. Every time it happens and every time I feel so guilty, so ashamed. Me, naked. Jesus, stuck up a tree . . .' Sister Arlyn started chuckling.

'You're right,' said Father Irvine. 'It's not such a bad sin.'

The rain had returned by Election Day but Sister Lindsey was as cheery as she had ever been. She bullied the minibus along the narrow sodden mountain road, making the nuns feel uneasy. 'So are you going to tell who you're going to vote for?' She looked across at Father Irvine, seated next to her.

'Does it matter?' he said.

'Not as long as it's the Nationalists,' she said, laughing.

Father Irvine craned his head towards the back of the bus. 'Is there anybody here *not* voting for the Nationalists?' Nobody raised their hand. He faced the front. 'You should get a job as a whip,' he said. Sister Lindsey laughed again.

The polling station was a school in the centre of town. After everybody had voted, Sister Lindsey called them together by the bus which was parked outside. From beneath a vast golfing umbrella she told the group they had exactly two hours to themselves in town.

Most of the nuns went shopping, others went swimming, and some stayed on the bus to read. Father Irvine and Sister Arlyn found themselves in a tearoom, sharing a pot of coffee and a hunk of carrot cake. They spoke about many things, including Father Irvine's decision to become a monk.

'My dad was annoyed I didn't work in his garage,' he said. 'He thought I was a "poof". So did I for a while. I never felt attracted to men but . . . I was suspicious of my calling for a long time. One day I was a young lad, smoking fags, drinking my dad's beer, chasing girls. Next thing I was heading into a monastery to settle down with God for the rest of my life. It *felt* right, but it didn't seem right.' He poured some more coffee; it tasted so much better than the boiling water he'd been forced to drink. 'Then I met Father Tom. He said there wasn't a day that went by that he didn't think about having a family, but that made his commitment to God even stronger. Feeling awkward was part of the deal.'

'And how did your dad react?' said Sister Arlyn.

'He said *he* felt awkward. Black-affronted. He never really forgave me.'

Father Irvine coughed and wiped a tiny trace of blood from his lips. 'So why did you become a nun?'

'Julie Andrews. I saw *The Sound of Music* on TV one Christmas. I must have been about seven or eight. I just decided then and there that I wanted to be a nun, even when I found out you didn't spend all day walking about, singing in fields.'

'I used to enjoy the chanting,' he said. 'I had a good voice, even when I smoked sixty a day. It was quite rough. I was the Louis Armstrong of the order.'

When they returned to the bus, Sister Lindsey already

had the engine running. She never noticed the massive sheet of polythene hidden beneath Father Irvine's cassock, or the saw and hammer he had bought from B&Q.

Back at the convent Father Irvine set to work on his kite. He explained to Sister Arlyn that they needed to bow the cross-beam with some rope so the face would catch the wind. He told her about the aerodynamic principle that would help the kite correct itself. She had never flown on a plane, far less heard of a dihedral, but could see the need for some sort of stabilisation. They also, she learned, needed some kind of tail to anchor the kite in the sky.

They worked in his bedroom, out of sight of Sister Lindsey who believed Sister Arlyn was reading to the old monk. Even though he was only issuing instructions, Father Irvine found himself exhausted at the end of each day. One balmy evening, when the hills glowed like cinders and thousands of rooks milled overhead like insects, he was joined on the porch by the Mother Superior. For a few seconds she too said nothing and followed his gaze, out across the unfurling green of the glen and beyond to the Cairngorms which still wore their cornices like quiffs.

'*Solitudinem faciunt pacem appellant,*' he said wheezily.

'They make a desert and they call it peace,' translated Sister Lindsey.

Father Irvine gestured towards the hills. 'This is where Calgacus defied the Romans,' he said. 'Mons Graupius. The rest of Scotland capitulated.'

'Why are you so interested in the past but not the future?'

'History repeats the old conceits, the glib replies, the same defeats.'

'Johnson?' said Sister Lindsey, trying to place the quotation.

'Elvis Costello.' Father Irvine gave a liquidy cough. 'Were you disappointed by the turnout last Thursday?'

'Why vote for the right to vote and then not vote?'

'Because people are greedy.'

Sister Lindsey smiled respectfully. 'My father spent his whole life campaigning for home-rule,' she said. 'He'd have been heart-broken. The turnout was just half in some places.'

'Maybe patriotism's as much a myth as the Loch Ness monster, just this big daft thing people want to believe in because they're too scared to believe in themselves.'

'And do you believe in God, Father Irvine?'

'Do you?'

'Of course.'

'How can you be so sure he exists?'

'I've devoted my life to him,' said Sister Lindsey sternly.

'Your dad devoted his to independence.'

'I have faith, Father Irvine.'

'I have faith in the sun rising tomorrow, even though I might not be here to see it. I have faith in those rooks being made from flesh and feathers. It's easy to believe in fact. It's the little nugget of doubt that makes faith what it is.'

'Is that what you tell Sister Arlyn?'

'Sometimes I want to tell her to leave here, find a boyfriend, have a family.'

'Is that what you wished you'd done?'

'I really don't think people choose to have family. When they're young they have all these ambitions. It could be working hard or not working at all but at the end of the day it doesn't matter what they want from life, it's what life wants from them, and that's more life, kids. At least we've made a genuine choice. We voted.'

'For what, though?' asked Sister Lindsey.

'For God.' Father Irvine looked again towards the hills. 'For God,' he repeated quietly to himself.

By the end of May, Father Irvine's cancer had seized control of his lungs – a spectacular coup. He sounded like a coffee percolator; his fetid breath curdled in his throat, discharging with an ominous watery rasp. Sister Lindsey had called the doctor. The young GP stood at the side of the bed.

'You would be more comfortable in hospital,' he said.

'Sedated,' said Father Irvine weakly. 'I'd be more sedated.' The doctor sighed and looked across at Sister Lindsey, clearly exasperated. She could only shrug. His tone became impatient.

'Believe me, you'll be grateful for the care you'll get in hospital. And you will only get it in hospital.'

Father Irvine reached across to a bowl of fruit at the bedside and tilted it upwards. 'Does anybody want a pomegranate?' he said.

'You're behaving like a child,' said Sister Lindsey, her cheeks flushing. Father Irvine let the bowl down suddenly. A pomegranate fell to the floor and rolled across the room. Sister Lindsey turned to Sister Arlyn who was standing behind her. 'You speak to him!' she commanded.

'I've got nothing to say,' said Sister Arlyn.

'I thought you were concerned for him?'

'I am.'

'Then talk to him!'

The doctor shook off his embarrassment. 'Excuse me for saying this,' he said to Father Irvine, 'but you're still strong enough to hurt very badly. You'll need morphine. God won't be able to save you from the pain.'

'I'd feel cheated if he did,' replied Father Irvine facetiously. Sister Lindsey could take no more.

'I'm sorry doctor, we're wasting your time,' she said, motioning towards the door. 'Give him his supper,' she said to Sister Arlyn, following the doctor out of the room. The door shut behind them. Sister Arlyn picked up the pomegranate and placed it back in the bowl.

'I was thinking,' said Father Irvine, 'maybe we should have built a box-kite. They're a lot more complicated but they're brilliant things, like a Chinese lantern but really efficient in the air. They don't even need a tail.'

'But we wouldn't have been able to hide it under the bed,' said Sister Arlyn.

'Yes, and I probably wouldn't have seen it completed.' He let out a long, theatrical gasp. 'We'd better get the paint out.'

The following morning was the last of May. The silver birch trees around the convent had already lost some of their vitality; the lime green leaves had grown dark and coarse. On the high tops the snow had receded, making the vast flat-backed mountains look like killer whales moving behind the mist.

Sister Arlyn pushed Father Irvine across the wet pink gravel of the convent forecourt. The kite they had laboured to build rested on the footbar, its sections screwed together. It wasn't until they had reached the cliff-top and started to unravel the long heavy rope that Sister Lindsey spotted them. She pulled away from the landing window and walked hurriedly down the stairs, accelerating towards the door.

The young nun released the kite eighty feet in front of Father Irvine. Her hair was shorn; the plaid which had once hung down her back now formed the tail. Father Irvine was naked. He grimaced as tried to control the kite. Blood seeped through the bandages on his hands as the rope again tightened. Both Father Irvine and Sister Arlyn were in a thrall to the shaking, twisting, refractory kite.

It was only ten feet above the ground when Sister Lindsey drew near. The kite, she realised, was huge, at least eight feet wide and twelve deep. By now Father Irvine was upright in his wheelchair, liberated by the force of the wind. He must let go, she thought, he must, but the old monk held on doggedly. The kite started to climb, surging upwards like a giant ray. It lifted Father Irvine clean out of his wheelchair.

As Sister Lindsey reached him she instinctively grabbed his legs, coiling her arms around his ankles. For a moment the kite's ascent was halted, but it seemed only to pause for breath. The pair were five, ten feet above the ground: too high to let go now. Father Irvine clung desperately to the rope and Sister Lindsey to his legs as the kite rose skywards, the St Andrew's cross painted on its polythene skin appearing brilliant in the sunlight.

The kite continued out over the crag, high above the tangle of heather and sedge grass, sweeping towards the clouds, towards the plump black mountains, and as it did so Sister Arlyn clapped wildly, bringing blisters to her palms.

FIONA GIBSON
Sugar Baby

Joe hadn't meant to thump his hand down like that. He'd just done it and now he felt stupid. Joe had been doing that kind of thing – couldn't help it things – more often lately. Like this afternoon, for instance. He'd been drinking his tea, making small slurping noises that Helen hated but he couldn't help (it was his way of testing the temperature; insurance against scorching). Next thing, Jeannie's shuffled into the living room in her zip-up slippers. She's holding a Rover biscuit tin. No, worse than that: she's holding a Rover biscuit tin and heading for the baby. Joe tries to speak but his mouth's full of fruit scone and all dried up; while he's chewing and swallowing and trying to work up some saliva, the lid's off the tin, a biscuit's pulled out – pink wafer variety – and jabbed into the baby's mouth.

You can't take a biscuit off a baby. Your life wouldn't be worth living. The child might have been only be 21 inches long but it could make one hell of a racket when displeased, not to mention that headbanging carry-on when things were really bad. Joe knew all about that. He'd learnt a lot about babies since having a kid. Come a long way since that horrible day when a girl from the office brought in her baby and dumped it on his lap. There had been no discussion about how Joe might feel about this; this woman had just thrust the child into Joe's arms, told him to support its wobbly neck and said, 'Play with him,' whatever that meant. No point in whipping out a compendium of games, even if he owned one. Joe froze on his swivel chair, baring his teeth, while everyone laughed and said how stiff and unnatural he looked.

But he'd learned about babies the hard way – by having one of his own – and he wasn't intending to have it stuffed with artificial colorants. By the time he'd got the scone down his throat and could speak again, he was so worked up that he shouted 'No!' or 'Stop!' (he couldn't remember what exactly; he just knew it was a short word, said too loudly). The baby looked up from the rug with his mouth gaping open. Joe could see some of the pink biscuit, adhered to the enamel of the infant's bottom two teeth. Of course he felt foolish immediately. Especially about the slamming hand bit. His fist had landed on a brown velour cushion and made a sort of *pff* noise. And it bounced back up again. He patted the velour as if he'd only meant to smooth out the wrinkles but had been seized by some involuntary jerking action. He knew he hadn't got away with it. Jeannie was looking at him, lips thin as cheese wire. His wife was on the floor, making a great show of tickling the baby's stomach. Was it normal, he wondered, to feel blood pumping through your ears, over a ruddy pink wafer?

Joe sipped his tea even though there were oily beads on its surface (probably off milk, he decided). It was cold so he didn't need to slurp it. But it was too late to get on Helen's right side now. Why wasn't she supporting him? They'd talked about this. Agreed that they wouldn't allow their child to be dosed up with e-additives and glowing fizzy drinks. They'd discussed it at length because they knew what Jeanie was like. Cake Woman. Sweetie Queen. And what had Helen done when he needed her support? She said, 'Mum, I don't think . . .' and tailed off to fiddle with the crocheted doily on the arm of the sofa. So it was left to Joe to make a stand. Otherwise, where would it end?

Jeanie smiled. She pulled back her lips to show shiny peanut teeth and said, 'The wean's hungry.' Oh, so they weren't feeding him properly? There was no evidence of malnutrition as far as Joe could see. The child had fat in places only babies have fat: padded hands, doughy thighs and neck rolls you had delve into to excavate milk residue. They might have been worried about the other thing – the fact that the baby rarely smiled and had never laughed (unless he giggled himself stupid in the middle of the night). No one likes being told they have a serious child, just as no one likes being told they look tired, and people were saying that a lot to Joe these days. Was it any wonder, when he was fighting the battle against refined sugars with zero support from his wife? As for hungry, pardon him, but he didn't think so. No one was starving in his house.

'And he's already had chocolate, mum,' said Helen.

Joe nearly laughed. 'Has he? When?'

'When you went to the toilet. Just a Twix.'

'Really?' Joe stared at the baby. He was surprised the kid wasn't thrashing about on the rug in a sugar-overloaded frenzy.

'Milk chocolate,' said Jeannie, stressing the 'milk' part as if it was somehow benefiting the child's developing bones or whatever calcium did (Joe couldn't remember; he'd have to look it up).

'Never mind what I think,' Joe wanted to add. 'You two go right on ahead. In fact why not pump molten chocolate right into his bloodstream? Cut out the middle man?' Joe didn't say that. He stared through the holes in the cream lace curtains where some lanky kids were swinging on a tyre. Too big for aimless larking about, he thought. They looked massive. But then, all kids had started to look massive since they'd had the baby. Everything looked different since he had the baby. Joe wondered if this was normal.

It wasn't this stressful with their new baby friends. Joe had been pleased to discover a group of young, like-minded parents living in the Old Town where he and Helen had bought their flat and they'd helped him learn about babies. Joe was a man who liked to know things and be involved; a new man, you could say, although he didn't like the way that term was ridiculed, implying that he participated in drumming workshops and thrashed about in the woods, eating pulses and hugging other men.

No, Joe wasn't like that at all. But he'd read about water births and was keen on the idea until they watched a video and witnessed an awful lot of screaming and thrashing about. He had to admit it; no one looked mellow in that video. 'What about a home birth?' he suggested. But Helen said no; doctors advised against it for the first child. She might need an epidural or anything.

Joe was disappointed. Did she really intend to allow

herself to be shoved around by doctors? Didn't she want control? 'They probably know a bit more than us,' she said, 'after all those years at medical school. We've only done a couple of NCT classes . . .' And what did she think these people had done at medical school that he – Joe – had helped to finance? Unspeakable things to human body parts, that's what. Only recently, a human leg was found abandoned in a bush by Law hospital and it damn well didn't walk there by itself.

In the end, though, the baby had to be whipped out by Cesarean. 'Air lift. Special delivery,' Joe joked to his friends, secretly upset at being cheated out of the drama of it all. He hadn't been able drive through town at 3am and jump red lights with Helen panting in the passenger seat. He'd stood in theatre, hovering at the head end, in a green cotton gown and a hat made out of J cloth material and clogs with 'Craig' scrawled on in fat felt tip. He held Helen's hand in case she fainted or started screaming; he was even prepared for her calling him terrible names and saying she hated him. But she smiled throughout, glassy on morphine. When they wheeled the baby back to the ward in his transparent plastic box, Joe had tried to push it to show he was involved. But the hospital porter had brushed his hand off. Joe had grabbed it back but they'd come to a swing door with only one half open and they couldn't get through it – not Joe and the porter and the cot at the same time. There was a minor tussle like they were fighting over a shopping trolley. Joe had let go and walked a few feet behind in clogs three sizes too big for him, clopping on the lino.

It wasn't how he'd imagined it. Perhaps this was why he

was so keen to do it right on the food front. People were changing, he was glad to see. Their new friends allowed their children to snack on rice cakes and breadsticks (if they allowed snacks at all) and said proud things like, 'Saskia never asks for juice. She wouldn't even know what juice was.'

'Bully for Saskia,' Helen had muttered. But Joe liked what he was hearing. He might have been brought up with an elder brother who worked in an ice cream factory and often came home with an arctic roll stuffed up each sleeve. But he'd grown up and taken a long, hard look at himself. Helen's mother should too. What was she doing, still rattling about in that big cold house with a pantry full of pancakes and scones? Joe was worried about her. He cared.

'I wish you'd try and relax, Joe.'

'Mmm,' he said. The Mitre was only three doors down from Jeannie's house but he'd brought the mobile in case something terrible happened. Better safe than sorry, he thought. He stared at it, an eyeball up against the LED display, in case there'd been some accident – a fondant fancy stuck in the breathing passages incident – and here they were, guzzling alcohol.

'You're making me tense,' said Helen.

'What?' He lurched away from the phone.

Helen looked round the empty pub, searching, Joe suspected, for something to talk about. There wasn't much you could say about a pool table with nobody playing or a barman wiping ashtrays. 'I'm sure she's managing,' said Helen.

Joe lied and said he was sure she was. He could have

pointed out that he wasn't happy about Jeannie bundling up the baby in three blankets – hadn't she heard of overheating? – but he didn't want to get into a row. Not when they were out, enjoying themselves.

'We have to do something about your mother.' He hadn't meant to say it; it had just tumbled out.

Helen fished the slice of lemon out of her vodka and tonic and bit into it, wincing. 'Do something about her?'

'Bring her up to date. Modernise her.'

He realised it sounded stupid as soon as he'd said it. Since they had the baby he'd had difficulty speaking. Sleep deprivation. He'd read in *Men's Health* magazine that an adult male needs seven hours minimum or awful things happen; irritation, loss of concentration, plummeting libido. And that was just the start of it.

'Modernise her, like a house,' said Helen. 'Fix her plumbing, do some repointing. Maybe stick in a dampproof course.'

Joe ignored this. If Helen chose to be facetious, that was her decision. He knew what he meant; stop her from living on Tunnocks wafers. 'She can't go on eating like that,' he said.

'And she's going to change, at her age?'

Joe knew Helen was right. When he thought about it, he'd never seen Jeannie eat anything that wasn't sweet or iced apart from that time they took her out for her 77th birthday. Joe had chosen the restaurant. The food was defined as 'Modern Scottish' and, although Joe didn't know what that meant, he had high hopes for their night out. Might give her new ideas, he thought. Enlighten her.

He knew he'd made a mistake when he discovered that the menus were etched onto slates. Then Jeannie asked for an ashtray. A polite young waitress with shiny black pigtails told her that the restaurant had a no-smoking policy. Joe had known that when he'd booked; with Helen four months pregnant and recently having given up cigarettes – as he had – he didn't want her in some passive smoking situation. He was disappointed that Jeannie had even intended to smoke. It was hard to give up; God, he knew that better than anybody. He'd tried some evil gum which he had to store in his cheek and gave him heartburn, then patches which made his arm go hot. He'd forked out for hypnosis and been rather put out when the hypnotist – a wispy Australian woman – had shoved on a tape and left the room. Not a bad way to earn sixty quid, he thought, having coffee with your hypnotist mates and laughing at the sap on the couch with his eyes shut, gasping for a fag. But it had worked (although he had found it difficult sometimes). He still had withdrawal symptoms: gummy eyes, tension around the brow region, the sudden realisation that the awful grinding sound was coming from his molars. It was particularly difficult that night in the restaurant. 'Wild mushroom and spinach filo parcel with a red pepper sauce and fragrant noodles,' said Joe, flatly.

Jeannie stared at her slate.

'Seared halibut served with a millefeuille of Mediterranean vegetables,' continued Joe, hopefully. He wondered if Jeannie knew what a millefeuille was. He wished she'd stop stroking that packet of Lambert & Butler.

'Goat's cheese ratatouille,' he added, his upper lip moist with sweat.

In the end, Helen had suggested her mother opt for 'plain fish' (which the waitress said would be no problem; and it shouldn't be, thought Joe, considering they were asking twelve pounds for a slab of bald haddock). Jeannie pushed it about her plate and said she needed the toilet but Joe knew she had gone to the adjoining bar; when she came back he could smell smoke around her hair.

Jeannie perked up when the puddings arrived and ordered lemon polenta cake. As they stood up to leave, Joe asked her if she had enjoyed her meal.

'It was different,' she said, bleakly.

Joe hoped Jeannie would be in bed when they came back from The Mitre. He wasn't in the mood for Helen's mother tonight. Their night out had ended up, not in a row exactly, but with Helen going blotchy around the cheeks and spluttering, 'God, Joe, she's 79. Do you expect her to start eating rocket?'

He was shocked by the way she spat it out. Joe couldn't remember the last time he had seen Helen angry. She'd gone dreamy throughout the pregnancy – probably helped by the chamomile and fennel tea he'd encouraged her to drink – and since the birth, her mind had furred up so much that she'd left her keys at the newsagent's, hurried back to retrieve them, then slipped them into the postbox with a letter. So what was up with her tonight? It was the way she said 'rocket' that hurt him. Implying that it – and therefore he and his salads with toasted pine kernels and, now you mention it, rocket – had ideas above their station. He was glad he had knocked back four lagers and two double Scotches, even though he didn't like Scotch much.

Jeannie opened the door in a brushed nylon nightie.

'We thought you'd be in bed,' said Joe, flatly.

'I thought I'd wait up. I've made you some sandwiches.'

Who honestly wanted sandwiches at ten past eleven at night? Joe opened one up and slammed it shut it again. It wasn't the tongue – he was vegetarian, not that he expected Jeannie to make the slightest nod towards his dietary needs – but the butter. Thick yellow slices. He knew about fat units from reading Men's Health. He was aware that in every Toffee Crisp lurked 13 grammes of fat and had been interested to learn that you could fry chicken breasts in lemon juice instead of oil. He liked the sound of that. He tried to think about that kind of food – light, modern – as his teeth sliced through butter. 'That was very nice, and now I'm all full up,' he said in what he hoped was a normal voice but could tell, from the narrow look Helen gave him as she peeled marzipan from her Battenburg, that it definitely wasn't.

Joe didn't expect to sleep. He thought he'd lie awake, worrying about what Jeannie had fed the baby while they'd been out; no doubt the child's blood sugar level was off the scale by now. It was a wonder he was sleeping. You'd think he'd be hammering the bars of his travel cot. But Joe must have slept because when he woke, rug-tongued from all the whisky and beer, everyone else was up. He could hear sizzling and taste fat in the air. By the time he made it downstairs, Helen had already eaten a dainty corner of Lorne sausage and didn't look even mildly upset.

'I'll just pack the car,' said Joe. How handy these men's jobs were. You could swerve the seeping cholesterol and biff about with a baby seat and travel cot; even check on the contents of your glove compartment.

Joe didn't know why he kept a packet of ten in the car. Somehow, through the night sweats and horrendous excema – his GP had even taken a Polaroid photo of his ravaged hands 'for research purposes' – knowing that the cigarettes were there made him feel better. He'd given up, so he wouldn't smoke them. But he could, if he really wanted to. He had a choice, and that made a difference.

He'd never intended to actually smoke them, he thought, feeling the rush at the first inhalation. And Helen would be deeply disappointed – but had Helen supported him when he'd really needed her? No, she had not. Joe breathed deeply, skin pricking, leaning back against the bonnet to steady himself.

Helen buckled the baby into the car seat. Joe breathed loudly through his nostrils. If he opened his mouth and exhaled normally, Helen would know he'd been smoking (since the moment of conception, her sense of smell had sharpened to the extent that she'd invent odours, sniffing through the flat after imaginary cat wee). So Joe clamped his lips shut. He nodded to Jeannie as she peered in through the open rear window, waving goodbye to the baby. It wasn't until they hit the motorway that he had the confidence to speak again. 'Helen,' he said, eyes flicking to the rear view mirror, 'why is the baby's face brown?'

'Mum gave him a chocolate finger.'

'Take it off him,' said Joe, cheerfully.

Helen didn't reply. Above the hum of the car, Joe could

hear another sound; an unfamiliar gurgling noise like a baby might make when tickled on the stomach. 'Is that our baby?' asked Joe.

'Yes, he's laughing. Weird, isn't it?'

No wonder, thought Joe. The child is delirious. He pulled in at the service station, even though he tried to avoid these places with their all-day breakfasts and baskets of fake bread. This time it was urgent. He reached back and took the finger from the baby; the chocolate had semi-melted so it slid from his grasp quite easily. The kid stopped laughing. He roared, of course. He screamed for nearly an hour until they reached the bridge when he fell asleep, streaky with tears, just as Joe had hoped to cheer him up by pointing out interesting boats.

Helen asked Joe to stop somewhere so she could check the baby was OK; surely crying that hard, for that long, would damage a person. But Joe didn't stop or even slow down. He wanted to get back home, he told her, where everything was normal.

'Joe,' she said, sniffing quietly. 'Have you been smoking?'

KATE GRAHAM

Debateable Lands

'*Although the basic line of the Anglo–Scottish border was settled in
1237, the problem of the "Debateable lands" was not solved until
1551*' – footnote in *Scotland: A New History* by Michael Lynch

*   *   *

Sometimes, you have to look at things obliquely to see them
better, or even look at them in a mirror. Sometimes, the result
can be disconcerting.

In the aftermath of the Gulf War, I puzzled how to
reconcile my belief in Kurdish self-determination with my
lifelong opposition to Scottish Independence. I was studying
in the Faculty of Law at Edinburgh University, and Professor
Neil McCormick had already lectured in jurisprudence. As he
is as well known for his Scottish Nationalism as his con-
stitutional expertise, I longed to discuss my dilemma with
him, but lacked the brass neck to chap on his door and say
'Hi! Talk to me about self-determination.' The dilemma
remains unresolved.

Why do I think it right that the Kurds should have their
own separate state, but not Scotland? Could it be because

Scotland already has identifiable borders, whereas the form of a separate Kurdistan would be sculpted from more than one unitary state? Or is it a question of the oppression and aggression which exists in relation to the Kurds but is absent in Scotland? It may be that I feel it is still possible to maintain the dual nationality of British and Scottish, switching between the two as circumstances require, and separation might mean choosing one to the exclusion of the other.

It would be about the same time that our television screens were filled with lumps being knocked out of Dubrovnik. Without the figurehead of Tito, the disparate ethnic and religious groups in Yugoslavia were falling out and into separatism. I had some vague recollection that the parents of a boy at school came from somewhere about there, but I had never thought of him as being anything other than Scots. The father's English may have been heavily accented and, as a result, at times almost incomprehensible on the phone, but the son's accent was uncompromisingly Scottish, and he was into Scots traditional music. It never occurred to us that it was not his music, not his tradition. It was the music he heard all around him in the folk clubs, it was what he played on his guitar. He made it his own, without, I suspect, realising that he was crossing cultural barriers and creating a cultural identity separate from his ethnicity.

Again, as I bought my paper in the local shop one day, the man behind the counter was reading an Urdu newspaper. I noticed a photograph of cricketers, and asked if there was anything interesting in the paper that day. He pointed at a headline and explained it reported the death of a number of demonstrators at some protest in Jammukastan – not a place I immediately recognised. I asked what it was all about, and he asked if I was a real Scot. I said I was. Then, he replied, I would understand. He proceeded to explain about the Jammukastan situation.

That evening, when I arrived home, I checked the atlas and had my suspicions confirmed. We were talking Kashmiri separatism. Like so many conflicts, it is generated by the preference for self-determination over multiculturalism. Where several groups live within the same boundaries, there is an urge towards exclusive occupation of zones. Where a group straddles the boundary, the urge is to break away and create new boundaries. Both urges reveal a desire for an externally recognised identity and an uneasiness in sharing space with different identities.

Some time later, when the US bombed Sudan and Afghanistan, we compared headlines in English language and Urdu newspapers. He could speak, but not read, English. I can neither read nor speak Urdu. Together we deplored the way certain newspapers seemed to be calling the Afghans 'Arabs'.

Last autumn, I toured round a number of the riverine oases surrounding the Takla Makan desert in Xinjiang, northwestern China. Fascinating though the journey was, I found lots of things challenged my thinking about Scots and Scotland. This had nothing to do with the recently publicised theory that the mummies found in the Takla Makan are probably Celtic. No, it was much more subtle than that.

It started after we visited the Urumchi museum, where many of the mummies are held. As well as the archaeological exhibits, the museum also has a large folk display. You must understand that China as a whole has fifty-odd ethnic minorities in general and Xinjiang Province has thirteen. Admittedly, in Xinjiang's case, one of the thirteen is the Uighurs, who form up to ninety-eight per cent of the population in parts of the province, and the Han Chinese are what you might call colonists or white settlers, but they are the dominant population in China as a whole, and that is what counts.

The Uighurs are a Turkic people who are first recorded in Xinjiang over a thousand years ago. The other twelve ethnic groups include the Mongols – descended from a regiment posted there about 200 years ago, and who brought their own women – and White Russians, who fled the Revolution. There are Kazakhs, Kirghiz, Uzbeks, Tadjiks, from the other side of the border. Borders, after all, belong to settled peoples and are inconvenient for nomads following the herds through the seasons. There is also the special group known as Chinese Moslems – ethnically Han Chinese but differentiated by the profession of Islam.

Buddhism arrived in Xinjiang 2000 years ago and a rich artistic culture developed. Between the tenth and fifteenth centuries, Islam took over, effacing Buddhism as it effaced the thousand Buddhas painted in the numerous cave-sites. In the twentieth century, Communism tried to efface Islam in turn, but has not as yet succeeded. Will it ever, now? In towns where there have been recent ethnic disturbances, the authorities do not permit the muezzin. The permission openly to practice one's faith is the reward for good behaviour.

That is by way of background. Now for the exhibition. It

was in two main bits. One part had mannequins dressed in the traditional dress of the ethnic group, the other part had a mock-up of a typical environment. This was where I started thinking, knowing that the new Museum of Scotland was shortly to open its doors.

Picture, if yez will, the outcry, had the Museum of Scotland given over a gallery to portrayals of a typical Italian ice-cream shop, a Chinese takeaway, a Pakistani grocers, an Indian curry shop. Yet, effectively, that is what the folk display in Urumchi did with Xinjiang's ethnic groupings.

Is such an approach racist or does it genuinely celebrate multiculturalism by rejoicing in the stereotypes? Perhaps there is a way to portray stereotypes in a way that does not demean the group concerned. The difference may be that Xinjiang has been a crossroads and a way-station on east-west and north-south routes since antiquity, whereas Scotland has always been the end of the road.

The nearest to the Urumchi exhibits that I know in Scotland is the black house type of display – and the Hebrideans can be described as an ethnic minority. There are also those in the Agricultural Museum at Ingliston – the herd's hoose, the bothy. If it would be offensive to portray the Italian ice-cream vendor as a stereotype, then why is it not equally offensive to portray the stereotypical Hebridean black house and its inhabitants? After all, I could see for myself on a daily basis that the traditional dress of the Uzbeks had been abandoned – our tour guide was an Uzbek, and did not wear those rather dashing trousers tucked into boots, but boring slacks, shirt and pullover. Is racism diagnosed in some proportion to the length of time a given ethnic grouping has lived in Scotland? I only ask. I draw no conclusions, yet. I only record that the ethnic displays in Urumchi Museum made me feel uneasy.

There is one fairly obvious parallel between Xinjiang and Scotland. Oil. Yes, and it's Xinjiang's oil too! A burgeoning petrochemicals industry is opening up the Takla Makan. The new road which crosses the middle of the desert north to south was built to facilitate oil exploration. The railway being built to Kashgar along the northern edge of the desert is not for tourism, but to carry the coal from the Tien Shan, which currently travels by road. The trucks are not large, and there are frequent accidents. It must be energy-expensive driving the coal in the quantities required.

The industry brings in oil workers from outside the province – predominantly Han Chinese. Unsurprisingly, that causes friction. Even the local Han Chinese resent the incomers, far less the Uighurs. The incomers get all the best jobs.

Does the existence of oil give the concept of independence a viability it would not otherwise have? Xinjiang is rich in resources, but (relatively) poor in people. The region has supported rich kingdoms and civilisations in the past. Other oil-rich countries have a status that belies their size, their general state of development and their population. It is easier to be independent if you can hold the world, or your immediate world, to ransom.

As a result of the new arrivals, sinicisation is creeping westwards along the northern edge of the Takla Makan. One hundred years ago, Russification was moving east, and many of the hotels in the region are still managed in the Russian style. One benefit of that is the large vacuum flask of hot water in the bedroom, to make tea or coffee. There is also distinctively Soviet architecture and symbolism to be seen in the western oases – like a hammer and sickle carved on an architrave.

Today, you can measure sinicisation in two ways. Signs are bilingual – road signs, shop names – in Chinese and Uighur. In places like Kashgar, the Uighur version is large and dominant, but the further one travels towards the east, the Chinese version becomes larger and the Uighur is relegated to tiny writing in a corner of the sign. The other indication is non-verbal and pits the camel against the panda as a motif on signs. Last autumn, the panda had reached Kucha, as had traffic on the railway. Further west, the camel still reigned supreme.

I never established if any Uighurs deplored the camel as a kitsch symbol like Scots despise Kiltie dolls and tartan pincushions, but would not be surprised if some do. Certainly, some of the Silk Road tourist tat can compete with the worst we have on offer. Nor did I establish their attitude to the opening of the region to tourists. It is a bit difficult if the only people you encounter in an area are employed by the state as tour guides and facilitators, especially when their employment gives them a standard of living vastly superior to the farmers in the oases or the nomads at the edge of the desert.

This situation is not unlike Scotland. One hundred years ago, after all, it was Anglicisation we were worried about. It is still recognised as a problem, but so is creeping Americanisation, as our history is reconstituted by Hollywood. But there again, I have still to get over the shock of Safeway in Fort William teaching me the Gaelic for 'recycling centre'.

I came back from Xinjiang wondering about the future of the independence movement in the province. There had been some press coverage of Chinese Government concern that the Taliban might support the Islamic fundamentalists in Xinjiang. Certainly, the Uighur population is strongly Muslim. Although most of the women wear headscarves, very few are veiled. There is also a steady stream of Pakistani traders on the Karakoram Highway to Kashgar, and regular flights from Islamabad to Urumchi.

Were the Islamicists to win independence for Xinjiang, would that strengthen the local culture or change it by imposing the strict rules we have seen in Afghanistan, Iran and Algeria? We can ask the same question about Scotland.

In an independent Scotland, whose version of the culture would obtain the state imprimatur? As things stand, most indigenous culture retains the status of a sort of sub-culture, below the UK state culture of Britpop and sitcoms, quiz shows and the RSC.

I remember an article in *Cosmopolitan*, years ago, on how women had only two role models – Madonna or whore. It is not a problem I, having been taught Scottish history at school, really recognised.

Into which of these two categories does one fit Flora MacDonald; or Isabella, Countess of Mar and Marjory Bruce; or Kate Barlass and Lady Douglas; or the women of Braes? These were the women who might qualify as my role models. For others, it might be the women who organised the Glasgow rent strike. Each of these women can be identified with an ethnicity and is renowned for action which endorsed or defined that ethnicity, but which could also be seen as acting politically or culturally. Who would, should decide?

Certain decisions were made for the opening of the Parliament. Would it count as heresy to suggest, for example, that there are others who could have sung 'A Man's a Man' just as well, if not better, than it was sung? And if it would count as heresy, does that not exhibit an intolerance of diversity every bit as insidious as that exercised by Islamicist governments?

Consider; I once heard a report on Turkey and the pro-Islamic party there refer to 'cultural Stalinism, of the type exercised by Edinburgh Council in the mid-eighties'. Even if you do not agree, at least you know what is meant. Political correctness is not restricted to all-inclusive language and the staging of plays celebrating homosexuality. It also takes the form of censorship, for instance if grants are withheld from theatres which dare to produce enjoyable entertainment that puts bums on seats in the dead of winter, rather than searing drama challenging the status quo and rocking our most closely-held beliefs to their very foundations.

'Would that God the gift would give us tae see oorsels as ithers see us' is the platitudinous mantra of the Scot. Sometimes, rather than looking in, it is better to look out. And it is not always best to look out at the most obvious examples – Ireland, Catalonia, New Zealand, Denmark, Quebec. Too often, when we look at them, we see only what we want to see, what we expected to see.

The other extreme is to look out at the really atrocious examples – that way lies the Balkans, Azerbaijan, Chechnya.

It need not be like that. We can look at other countries and see the similarities with our own, without denying our, and their, cultural differences. We can look at other countries, and see where they have gone wrong – even where they are about to go wrong.

And while we are looking out, and noticing these differences and similarities, maybe we can ponder what makes these differences, these similarities. What is universal and what is culturally, politically, linguistically determined. Music, after all, is universal, but the particular form a given performance or composition will take is culturally determined. If the music takes the form of song, part of the sound will be linguistically determined, by the language of the words used. In addition, what may or may not be sung about can be constrained by the dominant political or religious environment, or both.

Does culture ever have an existence that is not politically or linguistically determined? My schoolfriend sang, played and listened to Scottish traditional music, because he grew up surrounded by it. I expect he would have had the same response to the traditional music in Yugoslavia, had he been born and brought up there.

And guess what? On the road from Urumchi to Korla through the Tien Shan, there are places that remind me of Skye – the bleak screes, the towering mountains, the gravel beds in the streams. At the margins of oases, there can be an area which looks just like the dunes at the edge of the machair, complete with sheep, but lacking the Atlantic. And the cloth-capped men could have stepped from any photograph taken in the thirties.

As I wrote earlier, sometimes looking at things can be disconcerting.

STEPHEN LIVINGSTON

Choose Your Future

Building layers of music into sonic temples, the DJ lifts the revellers to new heights of ecstatic dancing. The beat throbs through the dance floor and up your limbs. You have to move, jerking your torso to the rhythm; there is nothing you can do about it. Your arms flail in front of your grinning, sweaty face in time to the snare drum as your legs stomp around to the thud of the bass. You've been dancing solidly for almost three hours, it feels like centuries. You begin to feel the need for rest and move towards the chill-out area for a seat and some water. Banging against other wildly grinning dancers like a crazed dodgem you try to direct your body, unwilling to give up the dance completely just yet. At the long couch against the far wall you spot Tommy and, stumbling over, collapse into the vacant space beside him. Tommy looks at you, vaguely worried, and says 'Are you okay?'

'Aye, fuckin' excellent.'

'You look like you've just went fifteen rounds wae Darth Maul.'

'That movie wiz excellent. Cheers for gettin' us the ticket by the way.'

'Nae problem. Ah'll go get some water, you stay here awright?'

'Aye Tommy. Cheers.'

You watch Tommy's back as he moves off in the direction of the bar. His shirt shimmers and shifts shade like oil on water, getting darker as he becomes more distant. It occurs to you that you can no longer hear the music, a fleeting thought only partially realised, then everything goes black.

Then everything is light although you think your eyes are closed and you do not know if any time has passed. Everything goes dark again.

The light returns and you flick open your eyes. *Where am I?* Think. *I can't.* Try. *I was at the movies . . . aye . . . and then the club with Tommy.* You are no longer in a cinema or a club, there is no one around and there is no music to be heard. In fact there is nothing at all to be heard. *Have I gone deaf?* You click your fingers to test. No, your hearing is fine and so is your sight. You do not recognise your surroundings but you can see them. You are in a large rectangular room, sitting in a chair against one of the long walls. The walls are bare and a bland, off-white colour adds to their insignificance. The only features to disturb the blankness of the room are three wooden doors in the wall facing you. The doors are closed. *Where am I?* and as if in answer to your thoughts a deep voice says, 'On the threshold of a new era.' The sound seems to come from all around you like the music at the rave but you know the club is far, far away. *What am I doing here?*

'It is decision time' says the deep voice in a soft, calming tone. 'Time for you to choose.'

'Choose what?' you say aloud, feeling perplexed.

'Choose your future.'

In your head you can hear Obi Wan Kenobi's voice begin a Mark Renton-from-*Trainspotting*-style rant. Choose the Union, choose independence, choose a devolved parliament within a federalised Europe; choose science and technology, choose genetic engineering, choose a luddite shamanistic archaic revival; choose currency, choose computer-stored credit levels, choose to barter a cow for four hens and a sheep; choose art, choose religion, choose chaos or fucking order, it's up to you. Choose your future. I chose not to choose the future: I chose the force.

You shake your head to remove the intrusion of these Jedi mind tricks and return to the situation in hand. Feeling more comfortable using conventional oral communication with the disembodied voice, you say aloud, 'Don't I get any advice on what choices are available to me for the future?'

'Through the doors you will perceive some of the possibilities that the future may hold, although all here is not as it seems. If you do not choose your future, it will be chosen for you,' answers the omnipresent voice in a tone you imagine expresses a vague disappointment at your lack of self-determination.

Obi Wan's voice pipes up in your head. 'Trust your feelings. Your senses can deceive you.'

Somewhat tentatively you approach the leftmost of the three doors and cautiously push. Nothing happens. You turn the handle, pull the door towards yourself and pass through the portal. Immediately you cross the threshhold your surroundings transform and you are in a huge, candy-striped marquee. A circus big-top is all around with people young and old squealing in delight as a clown capers around the ring juggling on a unicycle. When the clown comes face to face with you he drops the nine balls he had kept airborne and begins to wobble atop his precarious mount. Beneath the colourful, court jester's garb and garishly painted face are the features of Scotland's First Minister, his large nose coloured red like an old whisky-drunk. The clown addresses you in the clearly enunciated Scottish standard English of Donald Dewar while the rest of the crowd continue enjoying the show, oblivious to your experience.

'In the realm of politics lies our future. For the first time in almost three hundred years we, the people of Scotland, have our own parliament. This historic achievement came to pass not through violence and revolution but democracy. Democracy is the key to a brighter future. Together we can make this people's parliament work. Although geographically we are on the fringe, together we can put Scotland in its rightful place at the heart of Europe. We have the technology in place to move towards a direct democracy where the people have their say in all the important decisions that face our nation.'

The clown continues his political rhetoric for some time before he notices your interest beginning to wane, then he retrieves his balls and you find yourself back in the chair facing the three closed doors.

Your head is buzzing after listening to the clown's monologue and you take a few minutes to relax and digest the information imparted before approaching the middle door. You turn the handle, push once again and are less surprised this time when your environment transforms.

You stand on the verge of a beautiful wooded glade, around you a motley group of placard-bearing anti-road protesters shout abuse at workmen leaning against immobile trucks and bulldozers. There are banners hanging from some of the trees and in the lower branches of a mighty oak one of the protesters has chained himself to the trunk. On closer inspection the protester in the tree appears to be an unshaven Dr Ian Wilmut dressed in camouflage combat fatigues. This uncharacteristic positioning of the scientist from the Roslin Institute, famed for his groundbreaking work in cloning that produced Dolly the sheep, comes as a shock despite your earlier encounter with the First Minister at the circus. However, when the human barrier to the road's progress speaks, you are not surprised to see the rest of the protesters and workmen continue in their roles, oblivious to his words. He addresses you by name and you alone hear his praise for the powers of science.

'In today's society with the advancement of science and technology the standard of life can be greatly improved through the judicious use of our knowledge. Food production can be optimised by genetic modification, thus preventing hunger. Disease and the effects of aging can be eradicated through genetic engineering. Here in Scotland we developed and successfully created the world's first clone of an adult mammal. With these scientific advances Scotland is at the forefront of the new age, we can be world leaders in fields previously reserved for the minds of science fiction writers. In the future we can become the generation that does not need to die as our body parts fail. Through cloning, spare parts can be manufactured to replace degenerating organs and allow the mind of man to develop as . . .'

Truck engines start up behind you, drowning out the next part of his speech but you are left in no doubt as to the point of the inaudible words. Choose science for a better future. Bulldozers start to advance on the frightened protesters as they stand like deer caught in the headlights of an oncoming vehicle. Progress waits for no man. The lights fade and are gone as you find yourself once more in the bare room with only one door left to visit.

You feel like Mr Ben at the costume shop as you approach the final door, wondering where it will lead you and whose viewpoint you will hear next. Turning the handle you open the door and step through into a boardroom. Arranged around a large, mahogany table sitting stiffly in plush, comfortable chairs are a dozen or so business executives. The suits, a wealth of varying shades of grey, are listening to a charcoal-suited man who seems to be giving a fascinating talk on the company's growth in the retail sector over the previous tax year. He is pointing to lines on a graph displayed by an overhead projector onto a whiteboard. Getting accustomed to the way things seem to be working, you are not in the least surprised when the retail executive turns out to have the facial features of Bill Drummond, erstwhile musician with the KLF and self-styled art terrorist. The other business executives seem to continue listening to his presentation as he turns to you and begins his sales pitch.

'Profit, loss, buy, sell, consumer capitalism, it's all a load of horseshit. A game of Monopoly made real, a stupid game for stupid people. Take the money and burn it. The way forward for mankind is through art. It is the creation of art that puts man in touch with the divinity within and allows the soul to shine free. Imposed restrictions and shackles of materialism tether us to commercialism and force the eventual sell-out that is soul-destroying. Free your mind from these ultimately stultifying anchors and follow your dreams to attain self-fulfilment. Whether it be the painter, the poet or the architect dreaming spires and towers of the glorious word in myriad hues it has always been and always will be the creative mind that leads the way.'

A round of applause from the seated executives appears to signal the end of a successful presentation and a representative from the marketing division comes forward to give the next talk. The charcoal-suited art advocate takes a seat at the head of the table and you are back in the bare, off-white room. Only this time there are no doors and your chair has gone. The now familiar soft but deep voice booms out four syllables: 'CHOOSE YOUR FUTURE'. The walls shimmer and disappear. You are left in darkness.

A stinging pain flashes across the left side of your face as though you have been slapped and your skin feels prickly hot. Nothing. It is still dark. Then your face feels cold and something is moving over the skin dripping. There are shifting shapes in the darkness, getting lighter. You realise your eyes are open and you begin to make out the figure of Tommy standing in front of you. Becoming clearer you see he is holding an empty pint glass. Water drips from your chin and nose. Music is pumping out and the parquet flooring beneath your feet throbs with the bass like a point five Richter scale quake.

ALEX MAHON
Rocking the Chocolate Machine

'Goodall Directories, which name please?'

'Smith.'

'Smith, thank you and the address please?'

'Don't know.'

'I need the address caller, in order to find the phone number.'

'All I know he lives in Liverpool, near Tony's chip shop.'

Problem! Do I apologise and say I need more information, or do I give in to temptation and congratulate him on being the stupidest man of the week?

Solution! No. I bite my bloody lip and speak with a smile. This is how we're trained. And in case I forget how I'm supposed to react, there are plenty of little cartoons up on the walls with captions underneath to remind me. 'God Bless America!' Without your WASP settlers coming over and exploiting, sorry, teaching us the American culture, how would we have managed? In exchange for grants you give us employment, and permanent employment as you constantly remind us in your memos.

'Goodall Directories, which name please?'

'Johnson.'

'Which address please?'

'16 Prince Street, Derby.'

'I'm sorry, that number is ex-directory.'

'I don't care. Just give me the fuckin' number.'

'I'm sorry, sir, we don't list ex-directory numbers.'

'Listen you Jock prick, do it or I'll grass you up to your supervisor.'

I hesitate a moment. Do I need this job? Is it worth £4.40 per hour plus a bonus if I'm never late or off sick? I need to pay rent. I need to eat. And until I get letters telling me that I was successful at the interviews I went to last week, I'll have to stick with this one.

I raise a hand. A supervisor comes to deal with him. She connects her headset into the terminal and I hear him telling her how rude I was. When the call is finished, she tells me he wants to complain about me. Me. I've given this company five of its best years. I am always polite, helpful and manage to handle the calls within the required 'Call Handling Time'.

'This is not the first time we've had a complaint about you Jim,' says Janice in that patronising way she learned at some management convention – a place where human beings go in as free-minded, and come out as cult members.

She points to the wall and reminds me of the company Mission Statement.

GOODALL INC.

Be good at all you do, for that is reflected in how customers perceive us as a company. We must try our utmost, which means being helpful under extreme stress. This in turn benefits the company and ensures long-term employment.

I remind her that it is a 'Made in America' solution to brainwashing workers. By promising great things when you follow their work ethic. 'Lies, lies, lies,' I shout. 'We're Scottish, and have a different work ethic. Listen to yourself, for Christ sake!'

'There's no need to be abusive with me; after all you were once a supervisor. What happened? Felt out of your depth? Miss your wee union comrades?'

Sometimes I can answer quick as a flash. But instead I look at her, smirk and shake my head.

'I got fed up telling lies. How can I promote a company to its workers when all they do is fiddle the "Open Book Management" policy that it brags about? You should look on the Internet and see what they say about your company. There's lots of things you don't know about it.'

'Like what?' she says, in that sneering way of hers.

'Like for instance they're not even registered here, they're registered in their secret little tax haven in the Isle of Man. And they're taking over a company in Wales, paying them almost half their hourly rate but promising they'll make it up in bonuses.'

'Someone asked about that at the "Skip Meeting". Rupert said that was all union propaganda.'

'Well he would, wouldn't he? He's the Call Centre Manager.'

'Anyway, I'll be listening in on you in future, just to make sure you're keeping up our standards.'

After she walks away, her face is still imprinted in my mind, the same face that struggled to keep up the 'company standards' when I used to walk the floor and supervise. But by joining every social forum (out of working time) she managed to slime her way into the little nest of vipers we call management. There are a few good ones. But they too have to pay rent, eat and slave away until their secret interviews create a position for them.

It's funny. I've been out of school for eighteen years, worked most of them, but never joined a union: that is until now. I saw its dark spectre in the early Seventies when it seemed intent in bringing the country to its knees. Did it know that it would bring the working class to its knees? So here I am in this new Industrial Revolution. Cleaner working conditions perhaps than the last, but nonetheless a factory. We are the battery hens who must repeat the same process day-in and day-out. We're not allowed to speak to our neighbours. We're not allowed to read anything except company literature and even then we must do that in our own time. Keep taking calls, that's all we're good for.

'Goodall Directories, which name please?'

I hear a sexy, Kent accent request a few numbers. Her soft speech entices me to search the whole database thoroughly. She tells me I have a sexy accent. I blush, I'm only human and flattery gets to me every time. We talk longer than we should, both not wanting to let go. A voice interrupts us, it's that supervisor again, and I have to cut the call short.

'Jim, you're not here to chat up girls. I was half expecting you to say, "Do you phone here often?" '

'Excuse me!' I say sarcastically. 'I almost thought I was human for a minute.'

'I've a good mind to report you to Rupert. Would you like that?'

'Is this supposed to scare me? You seem to forget, when it comes to back-up, I've got almost every operator on my side, or "agent" as your little band of WASPs have named us.'

Her face screws up. Her jaws tighten in that angry way when you want to say something nasty but can't. Defeated, she walks away in disgust. It's tempting to shout some sardonic comment, but I won't. I'm not interested in scoring Brownie points, even if I don't like her.

The next call is a disabled customer. He can hardly speak, so I take my time and after much searching, find him a number. He thanks me profusely. It's the first time in ages that someone has had so much patience with him. It may be a boring job but it raises my spirits when I'm thanked. I know how he feels. Often some ignoramus has sworn down the phone because he doesn't understand my accent. True, after six hundred calls my voice gets a bit hoarse, and talking to my neighbour from Bridgeton doesn't help. It can be difficult to jump from slang to speaking very politely. And believe me, there are no contrasting accents than his 'real' and 'phoney' ones. Outside I tend to slip back to my old East End slang. It's kind of funny though – when I speak to my mates I feel as if I'm putting it on. Eight hours a day and five years speaking in a polite tone, makes you speak better 'n that.

At break-time I have to rock the chocolate machine. That KitKat, which is just hanging by a tiny corner of the wrapper, refuses to budge. Hardly anyone looks round to see what or who is making the noise; we're all used to doing it. I rock it more furiously this time, almost toppling it. Finally it drops and a loud cheer goes up. It was supposed to be replaced, we agreed that at the last 'Skip Meeting'. Oh! A 'Skip Meeting' by the way is where selected 'agents' get to speak to the management. This includes our Al Capone from overseas – Our Head of Goodall Mafia. Future Seconded Managers (Floor Walkers, people who have to fetch us water because we're not even allowed to move from our terminal), whatever, are present with their 'two questions which will be very easy to answer'. I remember the last time: I came prepared with three pages of questions so that everybody would at least know that they would all get asked.

We gathered round the table. Polite conversation was exchanged; I rattled my pen between my teeth. I always do this when I get nervous. We waited on the 'boss' to make an appearance. He was late. When we're late, we lose our bonus. When he's late, a simple apology is enough.

He began: 'I like to thank y'all for coming here. Before we begin this meeting I just like to say congratulations on your efforts for making this company successful.'

There were smiles all round. They looked at each other as if that one ridiculous statement had paid off their mortgages.

A well in the pit of my stomach, where angry words lay dormant, began to release a couple of expletives to my throat.

'So shoot!' he said.

'Johnny,' asked one of the managers, 'do you know when the chocolate machine will be fixed?'

A very tame question I thought, but worth listening to.

'Weeell,' came the reply, 'I was just on the phone only yesterday. I spoke to that company that deals with it . . .'

He looks over at the manager who asked the question and she replied, 'Cheapchoc.'

'Yeah, Cheapchoc, and they said they were looking into it.'

Another manager, who had been taking down notes, nods in his direction. This seemed to be a hint for him that he'd finished writing the answer.

'What's next?'

There were more lame questions. I could see that he felt he was going to have it all his own way until my turn came . . .

'Why is it that we earn less now than we did a few years ago? I mean this bonus structure seemed to change the minute we earned decent money.'

There was silence. I stared at him in case his eyes should wander round the room for an answer. He thought for a minute and then walked towards a flipchart at the back of the room. He picked up a marker and started to write some numbers on it. 'This,' he said in a loud Texan voice, 'is what we get from our parent company. But only if we achieve the target they set. This is what we could all get . . .'

'We?' I interrupted. 'Don't you mean "you", i.e. you agents?'

Now here was a man used to getting his own way. This one voice of dissent turned his face red. The others in the room shuffled nervously. The room became warm with the heat of fear and the static electricity that charged up the Texan's battery.

'I'm sorry, y-o-u,' he said as he spelled it out and moved his head from side to side. He continued: 'But this would mean every "agent" never being sick, or late and achieving the call-handling time of under thirty seconds.'

'Don't you ever get sick?' I interrupted again.

I ignored the 'tuts' and the sighs from every corner of the room. Besides, I was entrusted with their questions, and it would be me they relied on to get the answers.

'Yeah! Sometimes, I guess.'

'But you expect us never to have a day off sick?'

I could see he was searching for an answer again. This time it came from a wannabe supervisor – Roger. 'I'm quite sure you drum up enough business, Johnny, to justify having days off sick.'

I felt more expletives rise to my throat. They scrambled onto my tongue. Why is it, I thought, that some people go through life being absolute 'arse-lickers'? Don't they have any pride? What happened to being promoted on good old merit?

I wrote the whole thing down and turned to Roger and asked his surname. 'Why?' he asked curiously.

'So I can tell people exactly who it was that made the comment.'

His face changed from its smug look. Instead he sunk back in his seat and bit his nails.

I turn again to Johnny. 'You never answered the question about the bonus.'

'Well,' he said, and wrote some numbers with percentages on a page of the flipchart. 'You see, the average "agent" earns four per cent above the rate of inflation. And compared to four years ago that's . . .'

My mind switched off. I was never any good at arithmetic anyway but I do know we were all earning more money a few years ago. When he'd finished I played my trump card.

'Tell me something . . .' I pulled a wage slip out from my back pocket and showed it to him. 'How come it plainly states here the bonus is over £200. And here . . .' I pulled out last week's wage slip, 'and here the bonus was only forty.'

I sat back in my seat and watched him squirm. Inside I felt triumphant. So triumphant in fact, I looked around the room with a wide smile. It became wider as I saw how uncomfortable they all looked.

'Well, didn't I say never to rely on the bonus?'

A weak answer I thought. And then came the phone-call. I'd noticed the note-taker sneaking out the room earlier. Probably him, well rehearsed.

Back to the terminal, on goes the headset, passwords keyed in, the 'not ready' sign flashes, eagerly waiting to change. I begin my salutation, then a Yorkshire accent booms in my ear.

'Have you got Mr Jim's Autos in Barnsley?'

'Certainly, here's your number . . .'

'Before you go,' he interrupts, 'I was given the wrong number last time, can I get a credit?'

'No problem! How long were you on the call for?'

'About, twenty minutes.'

'About twenty minutes,' I scream down the phone. 'I find that quite unusual, I don't believe it took that long to find a number.'

'Are you calling me a liar?'

As well as a cheat, ya lying swine.

'Of course not. I'll just let you speak to a supervisor.' I put him on hold and call big Tam over. I know he'll just write his details down and chuck it in the bin. He listens, apologises, takes down the details and throws it in the bin. Good man! It's not that I'm against giving away the company's money to anybody but when it's so blatant they're lying, no chance!

While I'm taking calls, big Judy, the company babe, sits next to me. It's funny, no matter where I've been, there's always some girl who the men call 'babe'. I secretly touch the 'not ready' key and have a wee chat. She's French, from Antibes she told me once.

'Is that you just starting?' I know it's quite obvious but it's an opener.

'Yes. Nine to one.'

God! That accent. There's still a hint of it, even if she has been here ten years. I let the words slide all round my brain. Their softness send a tingle down my spine.

'Did you get up to anything at the weekend?' Before she answers, I picture her in a bathing costume – a see-through one – slowly climbing out of a swimming pool, hair all wet, every droplet of water sparkling like tiny diamond beads, her eyes asking – no begging – my permission to approach . . .

'Just stayed in and studied.'

'I like studying,' I exclaim, still staring. I blink the dream cloud out of my eyes and realise I have to back up the comment. 'Politics.'

'Politics. I used to be a bit of a radical myself, when I was at college, a die-hard socialist.'

'What changed you?'

'Well, when most of my so-called radical friends finished college and went into well-paid jobs, their ideals seemed to change as soon as they bought their first car and a flat in Hillhead. I'm studying business at Uni. It seems I've turned into a hypocrite.'

'No, I said smiling. Joined the real world.'

Before I can talk any longer she begins to take a call.

'Jim, here's a message for you, mate.' Big Tam puts a scrap of paper next to my keyboard. I glimpse over but Judy asks me something.

'I'm looking for a number in Ireland. It's a bank in Donegal.'

I lean over and accidentally brush past her. Well you can imagine what that does to a healthy man like me. I'm trying to find a number and I can feel Judy's breath on my ear. I find it right away and sit back down. I have to push the chair well under the table. Well, like I said, I'm a healthy man.

Before I take the next call, I glimpse at the note: 'Could you please attend the Skip Meeting at two o'clock.'

I thought after the last time, especially after me chucking it as a supervisor, I would never be asked again. I only put my name in the 'hat' just for a laugh. By the way, nobody knows what this elusive 'hat' is. You write your name on a piece of paper, put it in a box at the reception desk, sorry 'In Charge' as it's called nowadays, and hope you get picked. After all it means forty minutes away from your terminal – and in company time. Back to this 'hat' business. What kind is it? Has anyone famous worn it? Where is it? If a rich uncle, dying on his deathbed asks, 'Nephew, you can have my mansion or my Ferrari or even my twenty-two-year-old Judy clone-wife who'll constantly pester you for passion night and day, which one do you want? Either that or the old hat they use at your work. You know, the one used for the Skip Meetings.' I'll say, 'Please! Just once let me see the hat.' Well, maybe the hat and Judy. Judy, wearing nothing but the hat. Anyway, you get what I mean.

Now and again I look over at Judy. I can't help it. It's a strange affliction I have that makes my eye roll round to the side of my head. Strange how it only happens when there's a pretty girl next to me.

I take call after call after call. The monotony creates a wild imagination. Bodily I'm here but spiritually I'm lying on some beach on a paradise island. At least if money won't get me there, dreams will. Sometimes I'm scoring the winner for Partick Thistle. Poor Alex, burying his head in his hands just because we scored two last-minute goals against him. Ah! Well. At least he's won the European Cup. Now it's our turn. I bet he'll no come back to Govan in a hurry.

Call after call after call again. Each call blends into the next. 'Goodall Dir . . .' My eyes are aching. The uniform grey screen reminds me of my school uniform. Why didn't I stick in? Everything was boring. Thought I knew everything. Stuck here. Could've done better. Why doesn't someone phone me with a better job? Ages to lunch-break. Oh, Judy, take me away from here. You can wear that 'hat'. Fed up. Fed up. Fed up.

Eventually it's one o'clock. Lunch-break. Judy gives me a smile as she stands up. A set of ivory teeth shine from her slightly tanned face. 'Bye,' she says and gives me a little wave. I return the wave.

I brought sandwiches in, a couple of thin cheese slices in between two slices of lightly buttered bread. Doesn't taste great but it'll tide me over. We've got free coffee from a nice brown machine decorated with happy people sipping out of coffee cups. It tastes rotten but it's free. The tea's much worse. I sit at a table which has 'job pages' lying opened on it. Fridays are always good. As I peruse, some people sit next to me. I tell them I've been picked for the 'Skip Meeting'. I'm not there long before I have pages of questions come my way. I try my best to write them in my neatest handwriting.

All I hear are negative things about the company. Everybody's frustrated at the way they are treated. Some just jump on the bandwagon. Their lazy, don't-care-less attitude used to annoy me when I was walking the floor. Hardly any are in the union, but they have questions and lots of them.

It's two o'clock and everybody is there, except Johnny. The note scribbler straightens up his notepad and places two pens neatly on top.

'Are you sure that black pen works?' I ask him. No

reason, I just want to be annoying. His face reddens. He tries it just in case.

I see a space next to my favourite supervisor and give her a friendly nudge, 'Alright doll.'

'Don't doll me ya . . .'

'Now, now. Mind that temper.' I smile as she grits her teeth.

I don't see any friendly faces, only two managers, Call Centre Manager, the note scribbler, the love of my life and a couple of new wannabe supervisors, who've no idea what crap they'll hear the next couple of years.

Suddenly, in he comes. It's John Wayne and a couple of his posse. They're easily recognisable because they've got badges on. None of us wear them. Supposed to be for security. If anything, they should stop the stampede to get out.

One of the managers stands up to give old Johnny a seat. Another offers one of their posse a seat but he refuses: 'Hell, just treat us like one of you.'

God! Don't you just hate that 'I'm one of you' nonsense. You're not. You're much, much richer. Probably own some big fancy house in Texas, maybe even a ranch. They probably have a backdoor the size of Strathclyde. It must be murder trying to find your washing. I start rattling my pen between my teeth.

Johnny introduces his posse. 'Here on my left is Frankie Jackson.'

Oh, dear, oh dear. Frankie and Johnny. I cover my face with my hand, hoping no one sees me sniggering. The temptation to burst out laughing becomes harder to resist when I see how the others are smiling. You know, that kind of 'it's great to see you smile'; thank you for giving us a – slimes up the ladders, I'll kiss your Yankee ass – job. I miss most of what he says except some job title – Head of Goodall International 'Let's rip off the local yokels' Directory. He smiles. I give him one of my 'extra wide smiles', my special 'aint you a dumb ass' smile. 'On my right, we have Becky Goodall, the daughter of Tom Goodall, founder, blah . . . and all-round good guy'.

She looks round and smiles. Everybody smiles at her. I give her my wide smile. We all smile. She's quite fat, I notice. All those late-night fridge raids. Maybe it's a money belt. That tubby belly all papered with millions of dollars. My bloody bonus stuffed in her belly button.

'Becky and Frankie are here for a few days, just over from Texas to see how things are run in Glasgow.' They beam even wider, as do the others. All I'm thinking about is getting drunk that night, somebody's leaving do. Every Friday's somebody's leaving do. 'So fire away,' he says.

Just like last time. The same easy questions, the same reply: 'We're looking into it.' All the while my elbow is resting on one of my crossed legs, so I can cover my face when I hear the ludicrous questions and ludicrous answers. After forty minutes of this drivel, it's my turn. I'm laughing inside as I look at their anxious faces. Their weakness gives me a kind of power. All I really want to do is waste as much time as possible. And of course get all these questions answered.

'When is the chocolate machine getting fixed?'

'Blah . . . we're looking into it.'

'When is/are . . . why is/are . . . who is/are . . . what is/

are . . .' All answered with a hundred different connotations of 'we're looking into it'. I thought I'd mention the bonus, go through the usual routine, you know! The flipchart and the magic numbers. So I give a deliberate yawn. 'What about the bonus?' Yet again a poor excuse. What was it this time: accuracy, we never reached accuracy levels? Last time it was 'too many calls, not enough operators'. I was becoming so bored with the whole thing that I let my manners slip. 'So Sheriff, shoot!'

He rose to his feet. The blood rushed to his face. By this time I had uncrossed my legs and sat with my hands clasped behind my head. I can see his posse looking serious. Thank God their smiles were blinding me anyway. 'As you know the bonus is linked with performance blah blah . . .'

While he bores me with all the details I suddenly see a gasp-come over Becky's face.

'Johnny, if I may interrupt?' she pleads. 'If every agent gave a hundred per cent there would be no ceiling to the bonus. Working hard was the reason daddy became the man he is today.'

Something stirred in me. I usually never argue with women because I always end up losing but she managed to ignite a spark in me. Everybody has a spark. For some, it takes certain kinds of actions, for other it's certain words. Well, with me it's unchallenged stupid statements. Maybe it's my rebellious nature.

'When was the last time you worked, Becky?'

'Why, I've helped daddy in the office sometimes, why?'

'In other words, you've never really done a hard days work in your life.' I tell her with anger in my voice.

'I've sat down next to agents and taken some calls,' she tells me. 'Everybody I sat next to always said I was a born natural.'

'Well they would, or else they'd probably get sacked.'

'Daddy wouldn't do . . .'

Johnny interrupts, 'Is this the issue here?'

'Here, here,' says Janice next to me.

'OK! Back to the bonus,' I say, my voice much louder, body shaking ready for a verbal fight. 'So how come we're earning less money now than a few years ago?' I pull out a couple of wage slips from my pocket and hand one to Becky.

'Numbers mean nothing to me Johnny, only facts.'

'Why do you think people keep leaving this company? You must have the highest turnover in any Call Centre. This kind of business is supposed to be the future. But it's like everything else, when your type see a hole in the food cupboard, you poison it.' Rage was building up inside me. A rage that had been stored deep in my subconscious: a rage fuelled by years of being taken for granted. I stare at Johnny with my fists clenched. He sits back in his seat.

Frankie butts in. 'Hey, listen buster, back in the States we have guys more than willing to give some free time to this company. We thank them in our own way.'

'What nationality are they?' I ask him.

'I don't see that's quite your business.'

'What happened to Open Book Management, eh, Frank? I thought we could see any literature, or ask any questions about this company. Or does that mean certain questions, like the stupid ones here from your little gang of pathetic specimens dotted round this room.'

'Mostly Hispanic,' replies Frankie.

'I bet you don't get many applicants from the local residents. Not too easy to threaten to send back home, eh, Frank?' I can tell by the way he stands gawping, he's defeated. 'Don't you see?' I say, leaning forward. 'People like you give Americans a bad name. You're the only contact most people in here have with America. Just because you create jobs in an unemployment black spot doesn't mean that we all think you're all wonderful; quite the contrary, we think Goodall typifies an American company. Don't you have any sense of shame? When you die, you're going to realise that worshipping the almighty dollar was no passport to heaven. You do know you can't buy your way into heaven, eh, Frankie? And another thing, all this crap you have up on the walls, about 'what we can do for the company'. We don't worship companies. We see employment as a right, not a privilege.' All this time the room is hushed except for the sound of my voice. For the first time I'm being allowed to air my . . . our . . . grievances. I know it won't do much good. Companies like these don't care.

I leave this room of stunned silence and head straight for the exit.

BRIAN MCCABE
Something New

Jack came out of the 'Scotland' search almost as soon as he'd
found the site. He accessed some of the stuff he hadn't gone
into and saved it – he might browse through it another night.
He really should find out more about his ancestors, but after
working all day as a researcher for *The Human*, the last thing
he felt like doing when he got home was research. Well, he'd
found out something, at least: they'd got their own parliament in 1999. Strange. He supposed it couldn't have achieved
very much, coming so late in the day – just a decade before the
Unification of Europe in 2009.

He put the screen into mirror mode and saw himself
naked on the bed: his new cock looked good, long but not
ludicrously so like some of the cocks on the market. Only last
week he'd gone to a party where the host had come into the
kitchen with a really horrible 3-G, a special offer king-size
monster rearing from his thong like a late twentieth-century
dildo. Who knows what state that body part would be in
now? Such cheap and nasty geneplants were notorious for
turning bad in a matter of days. There had been investigative
pieces in *The Human* about the genetic transplant companies
who grafted horse genes on to human genes to produce such

obscenities. Sometimes the grafts didn't take and sometimes they did, but went wrong. He had read about cases of 'centaurs', totally unlike the proud, wild creatures from Greek Mythology they were named after.

Jack wondered if there really had been centaurs in Ancient Greece, but didn't feel like going into a search. He had a feeling that maybe they'd been made up, just to imagine what a cross between a horse and a man would be like. Now they were finding out – most of the cases he'd heard about were cursed with an impossible anatomy for the rest of their lives, which were always very short because of spinal problems. He had never actually seen a 'centaur', but he'd seen plenty of their mythical opposites: sitting in door-ways, their heavy heads sagging between their knees. They didn't die but went on living as a constant reminder of how things could go drastically wrong with 3-Gs – genetic genital grafts.

Still, everyone did it because it was possible – it was the future. What most people didn't realise was that it was also the past. When you asked the Genie – the gene-searcher – for a new body part, the search offered you something from the past, even if it used genetic elements from many different generations. What you were getting, after the virtual surgery, was a finger from the past, if a new finger was what you had ordered. He had sometimes felt disconcerted by the way a new body part could be grown with such alarming speed. Many people had expressed their misgivings about the fact that the genetic past was finite, and that people – including illegal clones – would eventually exhaust all their GO, their genetic options. According to some scaremongering prophets, the result would inevitably be a spiralling recession into the past, and the universe would implode.

Jack was aware of the dangers of 3-Gs. He had chosen carefully from his GB, his personal gene bank. It had used up most of his credit, but now he congratulated himself on a good investment. His new cock was pale, because all the accessible options in his GB were pale. He suspected that some of the more expensive options were fiction, invented by some Fantasy Consultant for a fat fee. They used the impossible to tempt you to buy the possible. His male ancestors – from Scotland, before the Unification of 2009, the Genie had been pretty clear about that – were pale-skinned people. Anyway, it was certainly a vast improvement on the one he had been born with.

The trouble was it didn't quite go with the rest of him, or at least with his other geneplants. But then there were so many, it was sometimes difficult to remember which parts of his body were his own. He'd more or less replaced everything you could see, and a lot you couldn't: heart, lungs, liver and quite a few bones. Some things had been replaced many times. His face had undergone so many changes, he sometimes accessed and enhanced ancient facial images of himself, searching for an original face. It was impossible to find his real face, because ultimately all that came up was the face he'd had as a baby, before his carers modified it according to their tastes. It was difficult to remove himself from their version of him, without a very expensive search. He had found only one image of himself as a baby: as naked as he was now, lying on a bed. It was the face that fascinated him: even although it had probaby been genetically designed to some extent, it had a haunting quality. Sometimes the eyes that stared at him from the screen seemed infinitely wise and thoughtful, as if the baby he had once been was looking at him across time and was trying to tell him something.

Jill was taking a long time in the aurum. He wished she would hurry up and come to bed.

His new cock didn't go with his hips, but maybe that was just as well, because in the last six months or so his bum had become wide, sagging and rubbery. The enormous crease between his buttocks was beginning to exude a peculiar, almost reptilian odour. The tight bottom he'd bought on impulse had lost its firmness in a few weeks, then it had spread at an alarming rate, becoming thick and lardy, eventually affecting every other part of his body – not only in an aesthetic way, as a horrible visual contrast, but also in terms of its weight. It had become a ponderous burden, a centre of gravity, and now he suspected that it was ready to go old on him. That was the trouble with geneplants – depending on the quality, they could age in anything between a week and a year or two. All the bigger companies were at work on the problem. Still, his new cock was good for the moment. He took it in his hand and was pleased to find that there was feeling in it.

He was also very pleased with his new breasts. Compared to some they were modest, small and firm and pink-nippled, with a delicate purity that made him think of rain and Scotland. He squeezed them together between his hands, then let them go and saw them spring back into their alert, outgoing attitude. It was reassuring to know that one of his distant cousins in time had probably grown such wonders all on her own without having to apply for them and pay for them. And he was getting her breasts before they had matured, before they had had to suckle babies. Who knows how many men had lusted after these breasts, just wanting to see them or touch them or give their mouths to them? Now they were his, but they were still strange to him – and what would Jill make of them?

She was depilating – he could hear the faint buzz of the depilator. She'd probably come out with a pudenda as bald as a billiard ball. Once she'd nodded off during depilation and had slumped in the seat. She had come out of the aurum without eyelashes and eyebrows and a drastically receding hairline. The next day she had finished the job and gone completely bald.

The buzz of the depilator ceased, then he heard the faint hum of the massager. So she was using the oils. When she used the oils on her body, it usually meant she was feeling adventurous. She had certainly hinted that tonight would be special, she was going to do something new.

Maybe, like him, she'd have one or two new geneplants, but he was hoping that it would be something else. He was hoping that tonight they would leave aside the VR equipment completely and experience real touch. He had wanted it since the night his visorscreen had been out of order and he'd had to rely completely on the network of feeling sensors in his VR suit and gloves. There was a name for it. It was called 'doing it in the dark' – people did it, sometimes, as a harmless kind of perversion. Real touch was something else. People didn't do real touch, or at least they didn't usually admit to it, but Jack was sure it was more common than *The Human* would have people believe.

Secretly, he'd wanted to touch Jill for a long time now, to touch her skin, and to have her touch him, to touch his skin, but he didn't know how to ask her for this and was afraid of how she'd react. He'd joked about it in such a way that she might get the message that this was what he wanted. Maybe she had, and maybe tonight this would be the 'something new' she had in mind. In any case he decided not to put on the VR suit and gloves just yet. But they were there, on his side of the bed, connected up to Jill's, on her side of the bed. He propped himself up on his elbow and popped the pills from their vacuum pack.

They weren't Instants. He'd gone to great expense to get a Deep Multiple Bliss for her and a Rodeo Rider – 'Hold on as long as you can!' – for himself. It was important that she took hers before he took his. He could wait until she'd had her first climax before he popped it, then she'd have her second before being drawn inexorably into his. And he certainly would hold on as long as he could. Maybe they would even come together.

There was such a range of orgasm pills and injections and sprays on the market these days, it was always difficult to choose. He'd done a piece about it for *The Human* – a round-up of the options available legally and illegally, with a bit of overview commentary thrown in about the morality of it all, which had unfortunately been cut because of space. Still, at least they'd kept his description of a group-orgasm he'd witnessed in a public park – a bunch of students celebrating the end of term – and they'd kept another bit in he liked about a woman he saw having a quiet but unmistakably pill-induced orgasm as she ordered some banapples at the fruitbank. Public orgasm had become a fad of life, and though it was more prevalent among those who were rich enough to stay young, some poor decaying people had started to do it too.

He laid the pills out, poured two glasses of Highland Water, selected some Ambient Scottish Music – it sounded like a Personal Alarm Device that wasn't working right – dimmed the lights, then pulled the sheet over his breasts. He didn't want the changes in his body shape to come as too much of a shock to Jill. It would be better if she discovered them gradually, during the dual virtual foreplay. Why was she taking so long? Jack wished she would hurry up and come to bed. His new cock seemed fine, but he hadn't taken it for a test-drive. Also, he was tired. He had had a hard day being groomed and packaged for his new site in *The Human*, which the editor had made clear was going to have to be about the most recent developments in Virtual Sex. If only he'd got the food site, things would be so much easier. It would just be a case of taking Jill out to eat and making fun of the food and the restaurant and the other eaters.

While he was waiting for her he put the screen into sensory mode, slipped on the gloves and the visor and indulged in some solo virtual foreplay. He could use his own body, with its new parts, to stimulate the images. He stroked a breast with the fingerpads of his thinly gloved hand and watched as the milky skin dappled with sunlight began to form before his eyes. He began to see and hear and smell and taste and feel them, the memories of the breasts.

It was a cold sunny afternoon. The breasts were in a graveyard. They were being fondled by a hand. He couldn't see the hand, or its owner. All he could do was feel it. Then something else came: something sweet and nurturing, smelling of skin and milk and saliva. Then he saw the baby's head, swelling beneath his breast. So he was feeding a baby. The baby sucked and sucked until it was falling asleep. But just as it was falling asleep, the baby opened one eye and looked at him as if from very far away, with that same wise, thoughtful look he'd seen in his own baby image – my God, was he seeing himself? Had they given him his own mother's breasts?

He reached for his water and guided the glass to his lips. In a piece he had done recently for *The Human*, he had used an analogy to describe what it felt like to do things in the real world while you were living in the Virtual – he'd said it felt like being a blind man at the cinema. That had been it.

Maybe he should find out where the graveyard had been.

He pressed the search button on his handset. He knew from his genebank transactions that his ancestors had come from Scotland, but since Scotland no longer existed it was difficult to know what to look for.

When Jill dimmed his visorscreen, he saw that she was lying on the bed beside him. He was a little disappointed that she she didn't seem to have changed – except that it was the first time she hadn't changed for a long time, and this in itself was a change. She looked exactly like the woman he had gone to bed with last night, but maybe he was being complacent. There might be hidden changes he would discover only during virtual lovemaking – maybe she had changed her sexual needs – and at least she was naked, rather than wearing any of those video transfers. Maybe he was right: tonight the 'something new' might be the thing he'd been craving. He could feel the heat of her body next to him. He began to unfasten his gloves.

– What are you doing? said Jill.

– I think I know what it is, said Jack.

– What what is? said Jill.

– The something new, said Jack.

– What? said Jill.

– Touch, said Jack.

– Touch? said Jill.

– Real touch, said Jack.

He held the gloves up by their spaghetti of wires before discarding them. He turned to her, his naked hands rising towards her naked neck, then he saw her mouth turning down at the corners with disgust.

– No, said Jill. Please don't, Jack.

– What then? asked Jack.

She moved aside to show him what she had brought from the aurum: two syringes, one filled with a bloody liquid, the other empty. A little disk. Even before he saw the GB logo he knew it was a catalogue from the Gene Bank.

– I want to choose a baby, said Jill.

IAN MITCHELL

Just You Wait, You'll See

We are privileged to bring you selected highlights from the Diary of the Future, by Dougal Macdour, the Nostradamus of Newton-on-Ayr

1 January, 2049

New Year celebrations were muted throughout the land. However, some hardy souls did manage to keep up the old traditions. With whisky at £45 a bottle, beer at £5.95 a pint and severe rationing restrictions in force, paraffin is becoming increasingly popular as a Ne'erday tipple.

25 January

Burns Night: for the disposal of rubbish. Be Careful with Matches!

21 February

Delivering the fourth David Begg Memorial Lecture in Edinburgh, Green Party Councillor Ms Deirdre Drear insisted that the joint long-term aims of the Keep Edinburgh Static Society and the Back to the Nineteenth Century Group were still in the forefront of council planning.

'We have come a long way since the early efforts of the great man whose memory I speak tonight, er, in. He strove manfully against the forces of reaction which held the upper hand in his times, but, since the city's total ban on the diesel engine five years ago rounding off the earlier banishment of petrol-fuelled vehicles, it has been easier for us for to look forward to the glorious day when all the citizens of our fair city will walk, cycle, roller-blade or skateboard to and from work. An important step along the way was the abolition of public transport, which had became an expensive and thus rarely used luxury.'

Unfortunately, the lecture was delivered to an empty hall, no doubt because of the inclement weather. Still, with high toll charges on all roads into Edinburgh, it looks as if the campaigners are close to victory in a city whose population has dropped to a manageable 22,000 and which offers thousands of job opportunities, especially in shoe shops.

There are still, of course, two fast, toll-free dual carriage-ways leading east-west and north-south through the city, exclusively for the use of MSPs and City Councillors.

30 March

Records were broken on the railways today. Both the 10.30 from Edinburgh Waverley to Glasgow Queen Street and the 10:30 from Queen Street to Waverley arrived at their destinations spot on time at 11.50. Railway staff and passengers alike were speechless. Fourteen people were taken to hospital suffering from shock.

4 April

High tides at Coatbridge: 11.48 a.m. and 2.17 p.m.

26 April

Rangers and Celtic met in the 27th of their thirty-match series to decide the Scottish League title. The game finished tied at 0–0, as have the last eight, but this time it was not until the 34th minute of the first half that the announcement of a full house at Hampden Park was made and the players could walk off. Asked why, as the season progresses, it is taking increasingly long for this decisive point to be reached, spokesmen for the two clubs reacted with anger and disappointment at spectator attitudes.

'Here we are,' said one, who preferred to remain nameless, 'close to the climax of an exciting season, with the series wide open, level at two wins each and twenty-three draws, it might even have to go to an extra five-game play-off. And now some Jeremiahs are beginning to carp about lack of interest. I have to say we are appalled at the lack of gratitude on the part of fans throughout the country. Between us, we have bought up fifty of the most expensive players in the world, if not in Europe, and all we get is empty seats for over half an hour and demands that the games last longer. Some of the players could get hurt, and they're tired enough as it is after a long, gruelling season.'

'That's perfectly true,' agreed his counterpart, also requesting anonymity. 'Here we are, the only two quality clubs in the league – well, okay, right, the only two clubs in the league – we have to play at Hampden because we've had to devote our two grounds, Ibrox and Parkhead . . .'

'Parkhead and Ibrox,' prompted his colleague.

'. . . Aye, right, right. As I was saying, we had to devote our former grounds to the merchandising of memorabilia and regalia and the like – replica strips, bits of turf, songbooks, stars' toenail clippings, players' hankies, all unused, of course – simply to satisfy demand. And now some of them are carping about value for money. I don't know, I really don't. I think it's all part of some media campaign, because the media have always had it in for Rangers and Celtic.'

'Celtic and Rangers.'

30 April

The Minister for Sport in Scotland announced that, because of the severe decline in the popularity of football, shinty was now being declared Scotland's First National Sport. Funding would be available to develop the sport in all areas and for both sexes, with special assistance being targeted on the country's ethnic minorities.

'Instead of going under that archaic and for many people unpronounceable (and therefore socially divisive) name of Commona . . . Camin . . . Caramel . . . well, I don't think I need be more explicit,' the Minister said, 'it will now be known as Shinty Scotland, and I am confident the SS will do an efficient job not only of bringing the sport to the people, but bringing people to the sport. In addition, I am pleased to announce the inauguration of a new competition, the Shinty World Series, and am confident Scotland will do well in it.'

Simultaneously, cricket has been banned as 'elitist, difficult to understand and, anyway, English'. Playing or watching it will now be a punishable offence ranking alongside fox-hunting and cock-fighting, as well as croquet and any other 'upper-class game requiring participants to dress up in white clothes'.

16 May

An unfortunate Japanese tourist was killed in a freak accident. Kneeling on the pavement to get exactly the right angle to photograph part of the façade of the Scottish Parliament Building in Edinburgh, he was struck by a slab of the stone cladding which had detached itself from the front of the building. 'I'd love to have been able to see that last picture he took,' said one of the ambulance-men called to the scene of the accident. 'But it'll take a while to dig his camera out of his skull, and I'm not sure Boots would take the job on.'

This is the fifth time a passer-by has been struck by masonry falling from the building this year, and the eighteenth since it was opened, resulting in nine fatalities, seven serious injuries and five heart attacks. In response to a question about the mounting number of lawsuits pending, all of them seeking leave to sue for damages, a written statement issued by the government reiterated the official stance that the building is perfectly safe and suggested that tourists and other passers-by had a civic duty to be more careful about where they walked and should try not to stamp their feet as they passed.

'There has been a despicable campaign by the media, and indeed by other groups and individuals out to make trouble, to attempt to discredit this fine piece of modern architecture, and we shall do our utmost to counter it. We refuse outright even to consider, far less accept such unwarranted criticism of what stands as a monument not only to Scottish democracy and freedom, but also to the workmanship of those who erected it in record time and despite the vagaries of the Edinburgh climate and union rules, regulations and restrictive practices, which last mentioned we, as a progressive government of the people, would not presume to call into question for a moment.' ('As for these frivolous court actions', a spokesperson added, 'we intend to pass legislation to ensure that they don't stand a snowball's, but don't quote us on that.')

8 June

The producers of *Take the High Road* have lodged an application for planning permission to have Ben Lomond moved five miles to the north. 'We have used the Ben as the backdrop for our title sequences for decades now, and we feel it is time for a change. It is not true that our cameramen are hampered by the mountain casting the wrong kind of shadows on the loch. This is a matter of genuine artistic integrity. Besides, change is the essence of progress, and culture and the arts must keep abreast of the times if they are to attract a younger audience.'

A spokesman for Scottish Heritage was quick to respond. 'Naturally, some people may at first be upset by this move. After due consideration, however, we have adopted a positive stance. We have no wish to be regarded as narrow-minded, old-fashioned fuddy-duddies, standing in the path of progress. It will be a major undertaking, but we are confident that, with good will on all sides . . .'

In addition, that stalwart of the long-running popular show, the cultural icon Mrs Mack, has frequently complained

that she has seen climbers on the Ben peering through tele-
scopes and binoculars right into the bedroom of her homely
little Glendarroch cottage to watch her changing her hat.

Can this be correct, or is it a hoax? Has Mrs Mack ever
changed her hat?

23 June
Clocks should be put back one hour tonight, because we all
forgot last year.

1 July
The 50th anniversary of the opening of the Scottish Parliament was celebrated in the newly refurbished Usher Hall in
Edinburgh. The First Minister, Cuchulain Ewing, in his
opening speech, welcomed MSPs (including seventeen members of the Ewing family) and reminded members that they
would be in these temporary premises only for about five
years while necessary minor running repairs, such as re-
roofing and the restorations of the façade of the Parliament
building in Holyrood were carried out.

After the ceremony, members paraded, carrying banners
made up of their expenses claim forms, to Edinburgh Castle,
where a celebration dinner was served behind closed doors.

4 July
MSPs re-emerged from their private session in Edinburgh
Castle. The St John's Ambulance Service and representatives
of AA (no, *not* the Automobile Association) were in attendance. The Parliament is due to reconvene after the summer
break, on November 6.

14 July

Early closing, Glasgow. Until 31 July (Glasgow Fair).

15 August

The Scottish Tourist Board is to be disbanded. A rather up-beat (or, as some observers put it, 'mildly hysterical') spokes-man broke the news in a television interview. He stated that the step had been taken on grounds of costs. 'Not on our account,' he stressed, and went on: 'In fact, our account is very healthy indeed, drawing as it does on tax revenue – a veritable Loch Ness of funding! Liquid assests, or what! Especially when one thinks of the Ben Nevis of the National Debt! No, at the root of the problem lie other accounts, those of potential tourists. They are proving inadequate to meet the costs of a holiday in Scotland. The principal drawback is the fact that petrol is now priced at £6.20 per litre, as our survey of all 143 visitors to this country last year reveals in no uncertain terms. They feel they are being pumped dry!'

He concluded, with a high-pitched giggle before being forcibly restrained and removed from the studio, 'But we are not downhearted. Our view is quite simply, *Qué sera, sera*, or, as we say in the tourist trade, whatever will be, will B&B.'

A television representative later attributed his unusual behaviour to the heat of the studio lights.

13 September

The Scottish Arts Council announced its allocation of funds for the coming winter season. As a result of the total withdrawal of its support for Scottish Opera, Scottish Ballet and the archaically named 'Royal' Scottish National Orchestra in the past five years, extra cash is now available, especially as these companies ('full of English anyway, despite their appropriation of the name "Scottish",' as one member of the SAC Board said) have now gone to the wall and are unlikely to pester the SAC again. In a determined campaign to foster genuine traditional Scottish cultural pursuits, and in an effort to be completely even handed, the SAC is awarding the sum of £23.18 to each of the following companies: Auchterwhine Peat-Stacking and Strathspey and Reel Society; Dalswinty Crochet Club; the Bridie and Bannock Festival; the 'Hello Duckie' Love-in and various ethnic minority group Bring-and-Buy events.

11 October

Glasgow City Council's Press Officer held a press conference to announce the 'exciting news of yet another feather in the city's hat of civic achievement'. In the face of stiff competition from major cities throughout Europe, Glasgow had won the title of 'The 2060 City of Something-or-Other and Something Else'. When it was suggested that this was all rather vague and tended to leave people with little idea of how to prepare for it or what to expect from it, he patiently took time to explain some of the problems faced by the European Commissioner for Junketing and Gravy Trains and the Minister for Freeloading:

1. With ten different such awards each year, it is now becoming increasingly difficult to discover, invent or concoct new themes for these special celebratory years.

2. More and more cities (and towns and villages) were clamouring for these honours on a regular rota basis.

3. Local dignitaries and business-people were finding their engagement diaries increasingly packed with demands for their presence on fact-finding trips, attendance at photo-calls for glossy brochures, appearances at essential events such as Cup Finals, Classic race meetings, gala concerts and dinners, brewery openings and luxury holidays in Florida, the Bahamas, etc., in order to endorse travel articles ghosted over their names. The result was that they required to know much farther in advance when they could pencil in the odd half-hour for visits to their respective offices, banks, factories and shops.

To combat these problems faced by very busy and extremely hard-working people who were carrying the flag for their cities, and indeed their nation, and at the same time to ease the imaginative burden carried by the officers in Brussels themselves, the European Commission had come up with an ingenious solution: it was simply awarding the title of 'European City of Something-or-Other and Something Else' well in advance in order to allow the lucky winners plenty of time to set up sufficient think-tanks, committees and working-groups to devise, either by their own efforts or by launching prize competitions, two themes to fill the apparent gaps in the title. 'In this way, democracy is served by allowing the people on the spot to choose what they want to celebrate, rather than seeming (as dissident voices delight in claiming) to have this imposed on them centrally by the bureaucrats in Brussels. The Commission does, however, reserve the right of veto.'

Asked when further information on the project would be available, the spokesperson replied, 'Oh, maybe about three weeks before the opening day of the event. Or, on second thoughts, perhaps it would be better leaving it until about a month after that date.'

1 November
Caledonian Post Office Counters are to issue a special set of commemorative stamps next year. 'These stamps,' a high-up official at CPOC HQ in Glenteuch Post Office and General Stores announced, 'are to celebrate Famous Scots of the 21st Century. Any suggestions?'

November 27
Members of the Scottish Parliament voted overwhelmingly in favour of a motion to suspend sittings in the Usher Hall, on the grounds that there had been several injuries caused by falling lumps of plaster and stucco from the newly refurbished ceiling. Instead, it was agreed that all parliamentary business would be conducted, thanks to a special channel provided for the Scottish Consortium of Commercial Broadcasting Stations, by radio phone-in. Since this would involve MSPs having to stay at home and use their own furniture during these phone-ins, it was agreed that a suitable basis of remuneration for this wear-and-tear would be an annual allowance on top of maintaining hitherto applying travel expenses calculated on an average over the last five years, with bi-monthly reviews to take into account current fluctuations in the rate of inflation and price-hikes by MFI.

Scottish Income Tax is to be increased by nine pence in the pound, back-dated to last December.

December 2

Because of the extension of Post Office holidays over the period from 18 December until 18 January 2050, it will not be possible for arrangements to be made for the payment of pensions and giro cheques during that time. Christmas has therefore been postponed until further notice and Hogmanay will fall on January 22. The main advantage of this will be that people will not be able to send Christmas cards, which they could not afford anyway. Last posting date for Christmas 2050 (assuming it takes place) will be July 10.

WILLIAM MUIR

The Second Coming

Who's next? God yawned. He was bored, severely bored. What letter are we at?

Peter gave him a pained look to let him know he was the bearer of bad tidings. S sir.

S, oh my's sake. Near the end of S? God asked hopefully. Peter nodded no. God checked his watch. Quarter to twelve. It's getting close to lunchtime.

We should try and get through this sir. As soon as possible. You do have other duties to attend to. Pressing duties.

I know, I know, God snapped. It's just I've been stuck doing this for over two weeks now.

Well sir, it was you who insisted on a yearly audit of your creation.

I know that as well, God replied. He stared out morosely into the twinkling panorama of galaxies before him. It's just that I envisaged someone taking over the steering of the ship by now. You can call me a fool but when I started I hoped I was starting a family business. God and sons. By now I thought I'd be able to relax a bit, spend the odd afternoon pottering around in the garden. The idea of tranquil afternoons in the garden seemed to stay with God for a second before he snapped out of his day dream and returned to the real world.

Okay. S is for?

Scotland sir.

Scotland, God mumbled to himself. Now, where is that? No, no, no, he insisted as Peter opened his mouth. I know this. His eyes shone as the answer came to him. Got it. He clicked his fingers. It's part of England, isn't it?

Oh no sir. Not at all, Peter insisted.

What's the matter Peter?

The Scots really don't like people making a mistake like that sir. Not one bit. Peter studied his notes. Geographically they do border one another but nationally there is a great divide.

Oh. God covered his mouth with his hand in mock embarrassment. Pardon my faux-pas.

Peter couldn't suppress his smile. Would you like some background sir? God raised one eyebrow. Peter continued anyway. Scotland was an independent nation sir until it joined in union with England and Wales.

Where?

Wales, sir. It also borders England. The three countries along with Ulster constitute the United Kingdom.

Ulster?

That one's a little complicated sir. I think it would be better to leave it until we get further along the alphabet. We should concentrate on Scotland at the moment.

Fine. Go ahead.

Population of Scotland is around five million. Up in the north, the country is mountainous, not quite alpine but fairly steep. The south is flat. The weather is usually grey, cold and wet. They're an entrepreneurial people. They've invented a lot of things but never made much use of them.

Lazy are they?

No sir. Just a touch cautious. By the time they've decided to push ahead with something usually someone else has nipped in, nicked or bought the idea and sold a few million of them around the globe.

Americans or Japanese I suppose. What else?

Nothing much. Their diet is pretty poor. They smoke too much and they drink too much. A lot of them tend to join us at an early age and they don't look so good on beaches.

What? Why?

I'm not sure sir. I guess they're not used to them. When the sun comes out they tend to discard their clothing at an alarming rate. Even resorting to rolling up their trousers. Their skin is pale to the point of transparency from lack of exposure so they immediately turn bright red. They're not like the Italians.

Yes, well whether that is good or bad is open to inter-pretation. So what stage are we at with the Scots?

Peter flicked through his files until he reached his current status reports. We have reached the fruition of our five-year plan to grant a Parliament for the country. Not a fully fledged affair. Just a taster. The Parliament is set up and running. I suppose, eventually, we have to decide, do we put them down for full separation from the English.

And the Welsh, God reminded him.

And the Welsh sir.

How have they done so far?

It is still early days of course but they're following a remarkably similar pattern to everyone else. The people they elected have generally reneged on their election promises, bickered about how much money they should be paid and fought over where their Parliament should be. They're even squabbling about where they should sit in the debating chamber.

They're worried about seating arrangements?

Apparently one candidate didn't like the idea of another sitting behind him.

Why?

Peter shrugged.

Was the candidate behind pulling faces at him when he wasn't looking? Or was the person in front worried about inky paper balls being flicked at his earlobes?

I don't have the details sir, however I believe the candidate you refer to does have a set of earlobes that would make a fine target for inky paper balls.

It sounds like a schoolroom. It's hardly inspiring. God's face sank into gloom. The people must be thrilled.

Exactly sir.

I suppose the question is, what are the Scots likely to do if we make them independent. Are they likely to begin a fascist dictatorship? Turn into a warmongering military machine that could threaten the peace and stability of Europe or indeed, the whole world?

I don't think so sir.

What makes you so sure? God asked.

From what I can gather sir they want to become more like Ireland.

Oh my's sake. God sighed miserably. You know what that means.

Peter smiled sympathetically. Yes, I'm afraid so sir. More theme bars.

Oh my, shamrocks and fiddles. They don't like fiddles in Scotland do they?

I'm afraid there are musical similarities sir. It's the Celtic connection.

God's stomach rumbled and he checked his watch.

Although the main wish for following the Irish model is to increase trade with Europe. Closer links to the continent. How close those links should be is a subject of much debate. Some are worried about losing their pound.

Pound of what?

The pound sir. Their currency.

God's eyebrows met in a knot of confusion. How can you lose your currency?

Europe has a new currency, the euro. Some in the UK want to change while others want to keep the pound.

It's a British pound not a Scottish pound?

Ehhhmm. Peter searched his files. I believe there is a Scottish pound. But it isn't accepted in a lot of places beyond Scotland, not even parts of England.

So they don't want to lose the English pound?

Peter kept turning the pages of his files until he closed it in exasperation. I don't know sir. I suppose so. In any case, as you suggested, you're not losing something you're changing it.

Yes, well, it's all very interesting. God said without enthusiasm. But I think we should make a decision on the future of the Scots and let them decide on the pound, whichever one it is. I guess we let them bang on with their Parliament for a few years. See how it goes. Then we'll review it with a view to independence. Fine. God slapped his hands onto the arms of his chair and prepared to rise. If that's all?

I'm afraid it's not sir, Peter said before God's backside had cleared his seat.

God's buttocks returned to the red velvet upholstery. He sighed. What else?

We have the Scottish representative of the HEAVENLY PARLIAMENT outside requesting an audience.

Why?

Peter examined God's diary. All I have here is, an audience is requested on a matter crucial to the future well-being of the nation of Scotland.

Do we have to? God asked wearily. It's so close to lunch.

I'm afraid we do sir. We owe the Scots.

In what way?

Well in the entire history of planet earth they've never asked us for anything before. Not once. The only nation never to have done so.

You're joking. God couldn't keep the astonishment from his voice. Why not?

Peter looked as much at a loss as his creator. No idea sir. An astonishing superiority complex. Pride. Stubbornness. All three. Who knows?

This must be extremely serious then.

I guess so.

He's not wearing a national costume is he? I can't abide another national costume.

No. I instructed the representative that informal attire would suffice. And it's a she.

A she, God said, surprised. Show her in.

Morag stepped tentatively into God's office. Her training shoes leaving a trail as clear as footprints in sand on the luxurious white shag pile carpet.

You may speak to God, Peter prompted.

Morag squinted at her type written speech. Determined that the reading glasses she normally required would remain secreted in her handbag. Lord the magnificent creator. The almighty highness of . . .

Ahemm. God coughed theatrically. Morag looked beyond her notes and shyly laid eyes on God for the first time. Please, dispense with formalities. God's stomach rumbled again. Carry on. Tell me what you want.

Well eh . . . Morag began

Sir. Peter whispered to her.

Well sir. Our small nation has been fortunate to contribute to the world in many significant ways. We've been blessed with inventors who have brought electricity, penicillin and the telephone to other nations on our planet. As part of the British Empire we shaped history and also brought peace to many countries in two terrible world wars. This is a legacy our people are justifiably proud of. But recently our country has fallen into a deep depression. We are becoming a soulless nation. A spiritual wasteland devoid of hope, devoid of energy. To our people it feels there is no end to this darkness. Only one thing can bring light back into our world God and I believe that only you can supply us with it.

What can I give you? God asked.

A world class centre-forward.

It took God several moments to respond to this. I thought you had Jordan. The big fellow with the teeth missing.

You're right your almightiness we did have big Joe and he was class but you're a bit behind the times if you don't mind me saying. He retired many years ago.

But I'm sure you had a big lad up front. Good with his head. Didn't he like pigeons or something?

I know who you're thinking of but he doesn't play for the national side anymore.

Ahhh got injured did he?

Morag bit her lip trying to decide whether to enter the intricacies of this question or not.

Something like that. Silence reigned while God pondered. I realise it's an unusual request your magnificence but we have good players, not great, but good. All we're lacking is a cutting edge. Someone to frighten the opposition's defence.

Still God sat deep in thought.

Peter indicated with a sweep of his hand that Morag should withdraw.

Morag bowed. I'll leave you now and let you make a decision. I'm sure that whatever that decision will be, it will be the correct one.

Morag slowly backed out of God's office. A gentle swish of wood against carpet as the door closed after her broke God from his deep contemplation.

Has she gone?

Yes sir, Peter replied.

Oh. I didn't realise. I was trying to remember the name of that striker. The one with the pigeons. God suddenly remembered his empty stomach instead. Anyway, he said brightly, lunch.

What about the Scots sir?

The Scots? Oh yes, of course, let them have their striker. Why not? A good footballer isn't too much to ask for since the dawn of creation is it?

No sir.

See to it.

Peter bowed. Yes sir.

Rain drenched the litter-strewn streets of Glasgow. Tommy lay in complete relaxation within the warmth and comfort of his bed. His wife lay next to him. Snuggled beside the heat of his body in post coital tranquillity. Hearts Dunfermline were the main highlights on the telly but the Old Firm goals were being shown later.

Marie stirred and kissed his neck. You know Tommy, I'm getting the feeling that I could do that all over again.

We haven't got any condoms left honey.

Are you sure? Marie searched the bottom drawer of the dresser.

Anyway, I'm a bit tired babe. Aren't you?

Marie returned to his arms. How tired?

Much to Tommy's surprise he could feel his energy reviving. A stirring in his loins. What about protection? He asked his wife.

We've already done it once tonight and anyway let's face

it, you're Scottish, you've done nothing for years except fire blanks into the box.

They held each other until their laughter subsided then made love beneath the ghostly blue light of a large twinkling star rarely seen in the skies above Scotland.

JANET PAISLEY

Howie's Land

There shall be . . .

Wisdom

Thing is, I'm standin at the shop. Thinking aboot it. Me an
Treeza, like. Aw right, I'm sparkin mad, tell the truth. No
getting tae see it, she says. No getting tae see it? I mean
whit's she on? Oh, I'm good enough fur whit she wants,
when she wants it. Good enough then, aw right. Doon the
canal it wis. First time anyroad. Standin up, under the brig.
No exactly yer honeymoon suite at the Ritz. But, fair doos,
best we could git. And, I'll tell you, there wis nae 'cannae dae
this, no daen that' back then. If a wummin could git a hard-
on, she wis it. Seventeen, like. Lassies that age just cannae
help it.

No that I'm sayin it wisnae me. I mean, got her gaun.
Still does. Just, noo she's got a hoose, it's aw aboot 'whit time
dae ye call this?' and 'when're you getting a job?' and 'don't
think you're hingin aboot roon the shop, swiggin buckie wi
they ither layaboots'. The night it wis ma buroo money.

'Didnae come, Treeze,' I says. 'Ken whit they're like.
Couldnae run a fag packet flat wi a steam roller.'

'Fuckin liar,' she says. 'I'm no keepin you. Buckfast king ae the Glen? Nothin but bad news.'

An that's me, oot on ma erse. No getting tae see it. Ma wean? No getting tae see it cause I'm nae use. Nae job, nae money. Buckfast king ae the Glen. King, notice. An she's no prood? I telt her. Wean'll be a prince then. Did she laugh? Did she wheech.

'Oot,' she says. 'Oot, oot, fuckin oot!'

Back tae ma maw's. Smile on her face.

'Telt ye that Treeza wis nae good,' she says.

So I'm standin at the shop waitin fur the lads. Street's bare. Trees're bare. Big fat moon stuck right up there. Like a kebab. Stuck on a stick. No getting tae see it? She cannae dae that. I'm doon the lawyer the morra, first thing. Get her telt. Get her sorted oot. I mean, wean needs a dad. Makes sense, din't it? She's oot at work aw day, wha's gaunae watch it? Me, course. Even if I'm at ma maw's. Cost her nothing. Jees, a wee snarl up wi the giro and I'm aff the books?

I telt her. Swear tae god, Treeze, I'll no touch a drop fae noo on. Gaunae be a dad. Get masell straight. Get a job. Nae booze, nae blaw. See youse aw right. Be there fur the wee man, when he comes along.

'Believe it when I see it,' she says. 'Nae buckie's same as nae braith tae you.' Doesnae believe a word I say, n'that's the truth. Well, watch me dae it.

Justice

I take a big swally. When the bottle comes doon, he's stood there. Swear tae god. A bluebottle. Oot ae naewhere. Well, oot the pigmobile that just sneaked roon the bend. That's whit ye get fur plantin a shop on a corner. Cannae see them comin. Place tae hing oot cause there's only yin road in and oot. Up on the apron, front ae the shop, lookin doon. Naebody gits by but whit ye ken. Just dinnae see them comin quick enough. So that's the frame. Yin big greasy bluebottle. Another yin in the motor, eyeballin us. An this yin, fillin the screen. Big gormless grin stuck on his mush. An me on ma lonesome.

'Got any blaw, son,' he says. I go fur the deefie.

'Whit?'

'Got any blaw?'

Must think I wis born yesterday. Wet ahint the ears. Right dumb cunt. Well, dumb is what dumb gets.

'Blaw?' Says I. 'Whit j'mean?'

'Aw, come on, son,' he says. 'I'm no efter yer hide. Blaw, ken? Just lookin fur a bit.'

'Christ, ye want tae go doon the toon then,' says I. 'See that Maggie's. Crawling wi stuff. Any ae them'll dae ye fur a fiver. No me, though. Sookin a polisman's dick's no ma thing.'

Tell ye the truth, I'm wishin ma mates'd hurry up. Bet they're hidin roon the back ae the club, huvin clocked the pigmobile. Waitin tae see if I'm gaunae get lifted, again. For the umpteenth time. 'No, yer honour, it wis not me what flung the brick through the off-license windae. I just happened tae be in the vicinity at the time. Cruisin, like. When it skimmed past, grazin my wrist as it did so, which is why I wis bleedin when the polis came. The six bottles of monk vino? Well, yer honour, the display toppled ower and I wis just tryin tae save . . .'

The bluebottle has decided no tae explode. Took him a while but he won the struggle. Decides I'm thick. Fine by me.

'Blaw,' he says. 'Rhymes wi craw, snaw, fitbaw. Blaw. Ye smoke it.'

'Och,' says I, haudin oot ma dout. 'Ye want a draw, huv a draw. Murder gein up, in't it?'

'MARRY-JEW-ANNA,' he bawls. Titch-titch. Lost it noo, husn't he?

'But it's Treeza huvin ma wean,' says I. Then I run. Take tae ma heels, roon the side ae the shop, up the lane, cause the next thing's ma collar felt, his haun in ma pocket and the cuffs slapped on. Station fur a kip and coort fur breakfast. There'll be nae dealin wi Treeza efter that. Nae hidin bad news in a place like this. Onywey, she's first tae the shop on a Thursday fur the Herald. Only reads the coort bit. 'Got tae keep up wi yer exploits,' she says. Tellin ye, ye huv tae admire a wummin that unnerstands the wey ye live.

The bluebottle's clankin efter me. His mate'll be runnin the car roon the Terrace tae cut me aff. I stick the buckie in the hedge. Right wey up, like. Need ma hauns free. Get it efter. Cannae stop. Five mair steps. Hedge stops. Wee waw. Up and ower it. Skelp on doon through aul Jamieson's gairden. Wee wave tae his missus at the kitchen windae, eyes oot on stalks, eyeballin big beefie hucklin ower the waw at ma back. Ower the fence. Doon the gress. Intae ma maws. In the back door, oot the front. 'Howie, is that y . . .' Cross the road, skitter doon the canal bank. Find me noo, ya dumb cunts.

I wander doon tae the brig. Two roads tae go if they come doon. Roll up, huv a smoke. Widnae want tae waste it, like. Ken, it's mingin, this watter. Things folk dump. Supposed tae be cleared up. Aw that millennium shit. Pleasure boats comin through. Parasoles on the gress at the club. Fur the millionaires, like. Ye huv tae laugh. Millennium fever? It's that aw right. The Glen club, millionaires playgrund? Enough tae make ye pish yersell, just the thought. Must be snortin the aul cocaine fucked their brains. Yachting on the Union canal? Just gottae be a crack-heid thought that yin up. Gets ye doolally, that stuff. And a holiday at her Majesty's. Better wi the buckie and a smoke. Mind, mibbe if I wis a millionaire. Just fur the dryin oot, like. Aw they dolly birds, models, film stars. Heids wastit. Stuffed intae private clinics. Aw they pneumatic tits. Intae that, man, eh? Could be worth a wee snort, right enough.

Aw shit! Here they come. Tippy-toeing doon the path like bricks through gless. Offski again, me aul pal. Up the bankin, no the track. Tellin ye, see this joggin lark? I should be getting peyed. Trainer fur the bluebottles. Lot ae moolah in that lark. Oh-oh, got their beadies on me. Aw right, chaps, show yeese how it's done. Ontae the road. Knees high, elbows up. M'on then. Bit of style. Along the path. Pump, pump, pump, pump. That's the stuff. Through the gairdens. Another wee wave fur aul Jamieson's wife. Ken, that wummin must be glued tae that sink. Mibbe he's got her stuffed. Wey her mooth hings open. Mibbe she snuffed it last time I went past. Just husnae fell doon yet. I'll gie her a wee shout the morra, check she's awright.

Haud on a meenut. Nae wallopin size twelves at ma back. Screech tae a halt. Look roon aboot. Not a dickie. Just ma hert boom-boom-boomin. Just the empty gairdens. Back windaes maistly wi their lights oot. Just ma mither's voice screechin.

'Howieeee! Just you wait till you git in!' That's fur the neeburs. Case they think she's no daen her job, like. Noo the door slam. Nice wan! No quite pit the windae in but near enough. That'll be ma da steered up. 'Slam it again, why don't ye? Shame ye left the waw up.' No in ma maw's then. No creepin up. Yin thing aboot bluebottles. They're cannae-creep creeps. So whaur the fuck? I go caunny, take a shifty ower the wee waw. Nuthin. Naebody. Must be awa. Shoot ower, doon tae the hedge, retrieve the juice and saunter roon tae the shop.

An there's the congregation. Aw the mates. Waiting fur King Kool. Wantin the hunkey-dorey. I'm squintin up an doon the road.

'They're awa,' Scratchy says.

'Fucked aff oot,' Fraser says.

'Gied up,' says the Boot.

I swing ma airms oot fur the big bow. Buckfast King ae the Glen. The Big Cheese. Ken, see if they hudnae clapped? Ma heid's doon and unner ma airmpit, I see the pigmobile pull up. Ma heid comes up and there's the bluebottle, blockin the lane. Fuckin smart fur dumb cunts, they twa. Yin at ma back's oot his motor. Noo there's the slope or the steps. He's gottae pick. Bluebottle's movin furrit oot the lane. Cannae go up the ither side ae the shop. Wouldnae get ower the waw in time. Gottae be the yin at ma back. Slope or steps. Move, ya bastard. Fuck it, he's no gaunae. Just gaunae staun there so he kin reach either yin. Bluebottle's close enough. Time tae shift. I go fur the flyin leap. Aff the apron ontae the road.

Widda made it tae. If I'd pit the bottle doon. Fuckin waste. Course it hits the grund, breaks, staggers me. Pigmobile's got the armlock on afore I kin steady up. The boys're daen their bit. Shoutin.

'Oy, he's no done nuthin!' 'We seen everyhin.' 'Better no be a mark on him the morra or youse are for it!' Jeesy peeps, whit am I gaunae tell Treeze?

Compassion

Doon the pigpen, the doin doesnae come. That's the usual, like. Whin they dinnae ken why they've lifted ye. Pit the boot in, hope ye'll come up wi somethin. Wi me, it's usually vomit. If ye kin splat the uniform, that does it. Gie ye peace then. Anyroad, it disnae come. Pockets emptied, shoes aff so's ye cannae kick fuck oot the door and interrupt them wanking ower yer charge sheet, then showed the suite. I'm dubbed up wi a suit.

'I demand a doin,' I shout as they slam us in. 'I know ma rights.'

Suit does not look too pleased.

'If that's got fleas, I'll sue,' it says. Wonder whaur he parked the yacht. I shout tae the screw.

'That BMW wis so mine. Fuckin broke doon. That's why I panned it's windaes in!'

'I'll have you!' says the suit. Oh, oh, oh.

'Come back here,' I shout, rattlin the cage. 'This suit's efter ma virginity!'

'Fuck you!' the suit growls. I lie doon on the usual hard as nails.

'Please yersell.' Mair at stake here than his aggro. Mibbe

a sair face wid help. Whit'm I gaunae tell Treeze? Somebody should tell her it's ma wean as well. No believe I got done fur joggin. Big licks this time. Bound over awready. Supposed tae keep the peace. Mair government funds reclaimed. Then I smell it. No ma tipple but.

'BMW, right enough?'

The suit's no sayin.

'Breathalised, eh?'

Not a word.

'You no watch the telly, then? The support yer local bus campaign? Booze yer blues awa and take the train?'

'Shut the fuck up,' says the suit. No deid then. Talkin again.

'Nice suit,' says I.

Nuthin.

'Shame aboot the socks.' Swear tae god. That wis it. 'Shame aboot the socks.' And he's up ma nose. Aul geezer tae. Aboot thirty five.

'Shame about your rocks,' he spits right in ma chops. 'If you ever want to get them off, you'll shut the fuck up first time you're told. Right?' M'on tae god, is this guy nuts? I'm chokin on the whisky fumes. That stuff's everlastin, ken. Anyroad, the bold boy quits inebriatin me wi his braith, sits back doon on his ain bunk, scrapes his hair wi his haun, calms hissell.

'What's wrong with the socks?' He asks.

'Nae holes,' says I.

'Nae holes?'

'Aye.'

He laughs. Swear tae god. Fit tae burst. Kechlin like a

wean. Rollin ower on his bunk. Insane. And I'm banged up wi him? Nae shut eye noo, like. He's quiet fur a bit, then he says:

'You going down?'

I think aboot the merry quip. But ye never ken. A suit might take ye up on it. And, tell the truth, I'm knackered. As weel as mindful of ma nuts. Trainin bluebottles on an empty stomach's no the trick. Gie him it plain.

'Nah. Fine, like enough. Anither pound a week aff ma giro. Still be peyin next millennium.'

'Tough shit.'

'Naw, see, it's Treeza an the wean. Says I've got nae rights. Us no mairried, like. Whit's that got tae dae wi it? Ma wean, in't it? If I dinnae git a job, I'm oot the picture, she says. Might as well be in the clink.'

The suit nods. Smashed, he might be, but he's no drunk. I'm noddin aff tae dream land whin he flaps his gums again.

'Want a job?'

'No me, naw. Work's fur eejits. Feedin yer sweat intae a capitalist state. Knockin yer pan in fur pennies so's some clapped oot nae use fur nothin boss that couldnae tie his shoelaces kin huv a posh hoose, BMW an a yacht? An whit dae I git? The poverty trap. Worn oot. Early grave. Fower letter word, that. Work. 'Sides, I cannae be arsed.'

'Hundred pounds,' the suit says. 'For doing nothing.' And then, awfy calm. 'And if you say a word, your throat cut.'

Integrity

Tell ye, I am sittin up by then. Stiff as a wee stooky, hairs staunin up on the back ae ma neck. Wonderin if the screws'll come on the first yell.

'You game?' The suit smiles.

The yell's stuck. So I squeak, insteed. Suit nods his heid. Bends ower. Slips his fingers in the tap ae his sock. Aw, jees. I'm banged up wi a real yin. Gaunae slip a blade oot, in't he? No much cop wi Treeze wi'oot a windpipe, am I? Never gaunae see ma wean.

The tap ae the sock rolls doon. Well, I am tellin you, I seen somethin then you wid not believe. Roon his ankle. Like yin ae they things page three's sometimes weer up near their interestin bit, this elastic strip. Like a bracelet made ae stickin plasters aw jined thegither, long weys up.

'Ten,' he says. 'Ton each.'

Fuck! I'm slammed up wi a fruitcake. Grand wrapped roon his feet. Fuckin bluebottle castle and I'm banged up wi a fuckin crack freak.

'If I'm remanded,' he says. 'They'll do a strip search. You're walking. If I'm sprung, I'll get it back. Hundred for holding. If I buy a stretch, you can sell a wrap on. I'll get the rest if and when. Deal?'

Aw, jeesy peeps.

Sheriff Shirty does his 'you again' look. I'm sweatin blood. Pound a week. Please, god, let him name a price. Swear on ma bairn's life, I'll never touch anither drop. Get a job. Be a dad. Make ma maw prood. Anyhin. Just say hoo much. I'll pay it. Pound a week. He pulls his specs furrit on his nose, peers at me ower the tap. Ma ankle's gein me gyp.

'Fine's don't seem to do the trick,' he says.

Oh shit. I'm mince.

'Work.' He says, like I'd say deid. 'Community service. Six weeks.'

Ken, there's something aboot a wummin when she's gaunae huv a wean. Big and kinna scary. That's ma boy in there. Somethin's gottae change.

'Got a job, Treeze,' I tell her.

'Oh, aye!' She disnae believe me.

'Doon the canal. Aw that millennium shit. Need folk tae clean it up. Got taen on this mornin.'

'Community service, is it?' Ye've gottae love a wummin kens ye that weel. She rubs her back. Jees, a boy wants his da aroon, doesn't he? Some'dy should dae somethin aboot that. Fuckin new parliament. Aw that guff. Whit ae they daen?

'Swear tae god, Treeze. An I huvnae hud a swally since ye said. On ma life. Kin I move back in?'

Faulds her airms, like. Planks the sooked lemon look on her face.

'Whit're they peyin then?'

In wi a chance! Suit went doon. Nae bail. Fuck knows whit he'd done. Some serious shit. Just gaunnae haud his message till he's loose.

'Hunner quid.'

'A week? That's shite!'

Aw come on, Treeze, gies a brek.

'In ma haun. Still get the buroo tae. Casual, see?' Kin mibbe stall her till some fancy lawyer springs the suit, dae a deal. Nae danger. 'Job mibbe only last ten weeks. A start, but.'

She sticks her haun oot, slaps it wi the ither yin.

'Hunner quid. Right there. Fur next weekend. Believe whit I see, ken? I've a wean tae think aboot. Nae room fur hangers on.'

Gaunae die fur this wummin. Swear tae god, I am.

Author's Note

The Scottish Parliamentary mace is inscribed 'There shall be a Scottish Parliament', and the shaft has four words engraved on it: Wisdom, Justice, Compassion, Integrity.

JAMES ROBERTSON

Six Deaths, Two Funerals, a Wedding and a Divorce

The door was open, just a wee bit. I could see light through the frosted glass. Hope rose in me. I pushed the door, just a wee bit further, and stepped half-in.

'Are you open?'

'Aye we're open. Of course we're open,' said the barman. There were two other men and a woman, sitting or standing at the bar.

I'd been up and down the street for half an hour, looking for a pub that would serve me. Most had posted signs saying that, out of respect, they would not be opening till one, or two, or five. The shops were the same. I imagined managers and owners had spent some time weighing up how much respect they needed to show before they could start running their businesses again. A bus had gone by, with a few folk on the top deck looking like they were trying to get home before a curfew. The bus was going pretty fast: there was no traffic and no one waiting at the stops.

But in Robbie's Bar the man was saying, 'Of course we're open.' I stepped inside, relieved. I could taste the IPA on my lips already. The place, it seemed to me, was an island of common sense in a sea of insanity.

One of the drinkers said, 'And we've got fucking cartoons on the telly as well.'

Our lives are marked by deaths in many ways. There are the deaths of parents, other relatives, wives, husbands, children, lovers, friends, workmates, deaths that shift in their shape through the years: unimaginable, unthinkable, unexpected, impending, devastating, liberating, remembered, forgotten. There are these private deaths, after which we may grieve in our hearts or perhaps shrug or even sing in them, and there are the public ones, those which trigger headlines, obituaries and funereal news footage. (There are also, of course, those public deaths of which the news is largely composed: massacred innocents, victims of war, starvation, drought, bombs, landslides, floods, fires and earthquakes, but here I don't mean those, I mean the deaths, violent or otherwise, of famous individuals.) Such deaths also touch us, separately and collectively, in different ways. They tell us about ourselves.

Sometimes these public deaths seem of such magnitude that they become points of definition for a whole generation, even for an era: people expect you to remember, decades later, exactly where you were when the news broke. And it's true, you do. JFK is the obvious example. The sole reason I don't remember where I was when Kennedy was shot – what Don DeLillo has called 'the seven seconds that broke the back of the American century' – is that I was only five and my consciousness was still – just – out of reach of the world. (Those were the days when I believed what my father read at breakfast was called a *use*paper because when he'd finished with it it could be put to all kinds of use – wrapping broken glass, soaking up puppy pee, drying out wellies, lighting fires.) The monochrome film of the car in Dallas, slow at first and then speeding away, the little figures in it jerking and slumping and climbing – that would come later, and become, in its way, as familiar as any other childhood experience of television. It would, indeed, be a bit like watching a cartoon.

But before that, little more than a year after Kennedy's assassination, the world and its public deaths had already made contact with me. One day at school, classes were suspended so that we could watch Churchill's state funeral on the television. I can smell the hall and feel the wooden floor we sat cross-legged upon, recall the way we were instructed to see what we saw as a momentous occasion in our history. A passing moment. Later we had to write about it. I still have the jotter in which I pencilled the following: 'We saw the cannons firing and the soilders marching and the actual coffin and we saw the Queen and the Duke of Edinburgh, the band played the trumbone the drums and many others.' At the bottom the teacher has written 'soldiers', and I have copied it out three times and received a tick for my efforts. I don't know if he missed 'trumbone' or just didn't know how to spell it either.

That was in February 1965. I was not quite seven. The world of Churchill and the war was still relived every week in the *Hotspur* and every month in the latest batch of *Battle Picture Library* booklets, but it was fading fast. Three years later, a boy came to school one morning claiming he'd heard on the radio that the dead president's brother Bobby had also been shot, and the same teacher who'd corrected my spelling, who would later become an evangelical minister in the Church of Scotland, struck the boy for spreading rumours and later had to apologise to him. Meanwhile the Americans were being beaten up by some people called the Vietcong; Paris was seething with student revolutionaries and the Beatles were doing drugs and psychedelia. My brother and I used to use the lid from our mother's preserving pan as a shield, and bamboo sticks from the garden as batons, and play at riots – police, any police, versus whoever. We took turns at being whoever. Maybe that Christian teacher was hitting out at more than one small boy who had better information about the world than he did.

The world was going up in flames and flowers and had a great soundtrack, but we lived in a quiet country which seemed unchanging, which a few years later the Paisley-born writer Gordon Williams would describe in his poem 'A Scots Burgh Boy's Dream of America' as 'a smalltime dump/where nothing ever happened and/there was nothing to do/And nobody had a name like Jelly Roll Morton.' I wouldn't read that poem till the early 1980s when it was possible to see that it didn't quite hold true any more: things *were* happening, *we* were changing too, though less violently and dramatically than other parts of the world, and under the weight of an oppression that was, well, barely oppressive by comparison with those other places. But by then I also knew that life was complicated and maybe you couldn't see things in perspective until you were at a point where you could look both backwards and forwards a certain distance. I had been through university but I was only just beginning to educate myself about my own country. Like Gordon Williams I'd grown up fascinated by America and finally I'd been able to go there. That, certainly, was part of the process: seeing Scotland from somewhere else. And I found out who Jelly Roll Morton was too.

In 1978–9, when I was twenty, I spent a year as a student in the USA. Apart from one week's holiday in Ireland when I was ten, it was the first time I had been overseas. I'd grown up obsessed by the Wild West, the Plains Indians in particular. There was nothing I couldn't tell you about Custer's arrogance or Crazy Horse's nobility, about white treachery and red heroism. I ended up in Philadelphia, hardly the heart of the old frontier. Over the year I had to re-learn America, the America that was, rather than the one I'd imagined. Inevitably, as the first, depressing, devolution referendum and then Margaret Thatcher's election victory took place without me, I had to rethink Scotland too.

By coincidence, within a week or so of my settling in Philadelphia, a death occurred which would only later have its effect on me. I knew virtually nothing about Hugh MacDiarmid: nothing about his politics, his poetry or his hard, unforgiving, unforgiven life. But between the obituaries and the reviews of his collected poems which were published within weeks of his departure and my arrival, I gleaned a good deal of information. In particular, some running subtext worked on me to convince me that MacDiarmid was hugely important, but that I did not understand why. In December I found a slim volume of his poems in Middle Earth, an esoteric downtown Philadelphia bookshop. The bookseller seemed both relieved and surprised to see it go at last. I read it through and through, then gave it to my American girlfriend with the portentous and pretentious advice that this book would show her 'another view of Scotland' – different, presumably, from the one I assumed she already had, or that I had given her. It was, in fact, a note to myself, for when I got home again.

Saturday 6th September 1997. I'd been determined not to be part of it, succumb to it. I was angry that you were expected to be silent, that at a moment when the country was supposed to make a crucial decision about its future the future was effectively put on hold by a media-induced hysteria over the death of an unfortunate, incredibly wealthy young divorcee. Before the television coverage got under way I was off, up Leith Walk to see if I could find a shop open, or a pub where I could sit the thing out. I walked towards the city centre but it was soon obvious that there was not much chance of browsing in a bookshop or trying on a new pair of shoes. The only shops still trading on the Walk were a couple of fishmongers, with their shutters half-down. Fish, I thought, stay fresh for no one, however famous, especially on a Saturday. And I remembered the words of Maggie Mucklebackit the fishwife in Scott's *The Antiquary*, chiding Jonathan Oldbuck for haggling over the price of a bannock-fluke and a cock-paidle: 'It's no fish ye're buying – it's men's lives.'

Jim Farry of the Scottish Football Association had been castigated in the media for refusing to postpone a Scotland international. He'd eventually had to bow to the pressure. Various sanctimonious shits had been offended by his question – Does the world come to a stop on Saturday? – a question which outraged them chiefly because there was only one obvious answer to it, as the crowded supermarkets and shopping centres that afternoon would testify: most of them would have kicked off by three o'clock, and some would stay open late for extra time, to make up for the sales lost when they and their customers were mourning Diana. The not altogether strange thing about Farry's crucifixion in the press was that I had yet to meet anyone who didn't agree with him.

There was, I believe, a silent majority who thought that the Diana thing was so over the top as to be on another planet. One has to be careful with terms like 'silent majority' – a phrase coined by Richard Nixon in 1969, when, in appealing for support for the war in Vietnam, his ploy was to persuade his fellow Americans that most of them, out there in front of their TV sets, were just as decent, honest, courageous and fully prepared to do the right thing as he was. Nevertheless, I was sure at the time, and as time passes I become even surer, that a sizeable majority of people in Scotland thought that the rest of the 'nation', led or at least encouraged by the newly elected Labour government, had taken leave of their senses. The world was going up in flowers again, but the trail of cellophane and wilting stems thinned out rapidly the further north one got. But this is probably a false impression in one sense: I suspect a major percentage of people in England, Wales and everywhere else also thought they were the only ones for whom all four wheels were still on the trolley of life. But it was virtually impossible to say so, and for those working for a Yes vote in the referendum campaign, it was unbelievably frustrating to be forced to take a week off. It was, however, necessary: there were elements in the media who would have slavered over the opportunity to taint the pro-parliament campaign with images of Scotland Forward workers out on the street, refusing to suspend their politicking while a nation, *the* nation, mourned.

However, maybe the hiatus was not, in the end, detrimental to the cause. On the Monday, when things were allowed to happen again, I was leafleting tenements and tower blocks in Leith. At the first intercom I buzzed to get entry to a stair, a disembodied voice demanded angrily why I wanted in. When I explained, the voice exploded in my ear, 'Oh thank Christ for that! Back to bloody reality.' I think it was at that point, as the lock was released, that I knew everything was going to be all right.

Another refugee came into the bar when I was halfway through my pint, watching Donald Duck instead of Diana's funeral, and started telling Diana jokes. They weren't very funny but we laughed, a little. I thought of the taxi driver, who in the small hours of the previous Sunday had first given me the news of the car crash in Paris. Stupidly, I'd said, 'You're kidding.' 'No,' he said, 'I'm no. I mean, I'm no royalist, but I wouldnae joke about a thing like that.' In Robbie's Bar, after seven days in which there had been non-stop, wall-to-wall coverage of Diana's death to the exclusion of virtually everything else – Mother Teresa died the same week and was lucky to get a passing mention – it felt like we'd earned a bad joke or two. We were a wee knot of protestors, with nothing to protest against except that we shouldn't have to feel like strangers in a strange land. We were in our own place, yet out of place. Or were we, really? All I know is that it felt necessary to miss seeing what everybody else was seeing.

In 1981 I'd also managed, more by accident than planning, to miss the fairy-tale wedding to which that day's funeral was like a weird, mocking mirror image. I'd been in Western Australia, hundreds of miles into the outback, working on a project for a mining company that, in retrospect, I'm sure must have been a tax scam. We drilled and sampled our way across a barren sheep station, ostensibly prospecting for gold and other minerals, and at night played cards, drank a lot of beer and complained about the cook. I spent long hours alone at the bottom of twelve-foot deep costeans gouged out of the desert, scraping bits of the walls into muslin bags, shifting soil like some solitary insect in the red earth while the sun beat down from a sky so blue it looked solid. I couldn't have been further from the royal occasion if I'd tried. It was the perfect place for a republican to absent himself from history.

You cannot do that. You cannot evade events; they will find you again at some stage and surprise you with their familiarity. L.P. Hartley's well-worn phrase about the past being a foreign country has been rattling around in my head for years: *they do things differently there*. Seductive but misleading. Yes, they do; but *they* are also *us*, we are them. We had better not discard the past too lightly. It is all we have of ourselves.

Strip away the media hype, the excess, and Diana was Diana. It is too easy, too patronising, to dismiss the people who were affected by her as somehow having been duped. I could not feel the way they felt; never could, never will. But, on reflection I think I know *how* they felt.

December 1980, six months before the royal wedding. I

was working in Sydney fish market, packing ice for a guy called John Baker: the kind of blunt-bodied Australian businessman who worked himself as hard as he worked his employees and thought the *Guardian Weekly* was a communist propaganda sheet. 'Every bastard and his dog wants ice', was his refrain between taking orders for four thousand bags of the stuff and cursing the ice-making equipment when it broke down. He had three teams of us working shifts round the clock. It was tough, tough physical work but it paid well and I wasn't going to do it for life. One evening as I came off the backshift one of the guys coming on for the night said, 'Did you hear about John Lennon?' We hadn't heard anything in there, under the roar of the ice coming down the chute.

The world was as stunned by Lennon's murder as it would be by Diana's death. The media just didn't know how to crank up the volume in 1980. Nevertheless, all day long next day some radio stations played nothing but Beatles and Lennon music. The same comment that would be made about Diana was repeatedly made about John: he was just 'starting over', as the song went, after a rocky period. He was a very different icon to her: a wise-cracking, peelie-wally, moody, funny, working-class, cynical, naive, not very beautiful writer of good, sometimes beautiful songs. He'd survived the break-up of the group in 1970. You assumed he would always be around.

I was too young for the Beatles really, and yet I kind of grew up with them. At four I was in a band, playing the tin drum, while my brother and his pal played the tennis rackets, to 'I Want To Hold Your Hand' on the gramophone. On the drum we'd painted the name The Three Spiders. It did feel, when John was killed for no reason other than that he was who he was, as though something very personal had been removed from my life.

Next morning, on my way to work, there was some new graffiti on a wall near the docks, a line from one of his songs: *after all, I'm only sleeping*. That was the thing about him. He wrote damn good lyrics, they captured the mood of the times. But the world didn't stop: the fish needed ice.

Like the numbness I felt, that graffiti, I suppose, will have faded away by now.

During the campaign for the first ever democratic election to a Scottish parliament this spring, much was made of the term *divorce*. Don't do it, Labour told us; don't go down the highway to acrimony recommended by the SNP. (In 1981 feminists and anti-royalists had sported badges saying Don't Do It Di, meaning don't marry a fusty 32-year-old layabout, but this advice had been ignored.) There was an unspoken implication in Labour's plea that divorce was, in essence or principle or something, a Bad Thing, that independence was also a Bad Thing, and that the electorate would understand and agree with this. It ignored the fact that for many unhappy, abused, unfulfilled, emotionally starved or economically deprived people divorce is very far from being a Bad Thing, and that marriage is not always motivated only by mutual love and understanding. There is a story, possibly apocryphal, that on the day the Scots parliament finally approved the Union in January 1707, somebody broke into the bell-tower of St Giles and the lament 'Why Should I Be Sad on My Wedding Day?' rang out over Edinburgh. As it turned out, Labour romped home in the election and divorce proceedings, whatever they might have entailed, are not yet under way.

Nevertheless, it is undeniable that the establishment of a Scottish parliament marks a division of some kind; between one political age and another, for a start. The scaremongering about an Anglo-Scottish divorce depended on no attention being paid to the fact that all the constituent countries, provinces and principalities of the British Isles had entered a new era of relationships, of which the Scotland-England one was only the most obvious. But could one also discern, in the final victory of those who had worked so long for a significant measure of Scottish self-determination, a division between political *styles*, even perhaps between sets of values? Among those who did not live to see what was, in Donald Dewar's words, first a hope, then a belief, then a promise, become a reality, was the man who had called the whole process 'unfinished business'. The man who, as Dewar said at his funeral, could start a party in an empty room, and often did, missed the party that finished the business. The quiet, restrained, almost universal sorrow which greeted John Smith's death in May 1994 has never quite gone away, and one of the reasons, perhaps, is that with his passing it seemed a certain loyalty to principles had also gone out of Labour politics. Maybe, possibly, the parliament can be a modern institution in a country renewed and invigorated by old principles.

Maybe this is too romantic a notion. Still, it was notable that the first new public building of cultural importance to be completed in this fresh era was neither a parliament, nor a conference centre, nor a memorial, but a poetry library. Of all the arts, poetry might be considered to have less to do with the anti-cultural values of the Thatcherite years than any other; and here was a structure devoted to it rising out of a building site a stone's throw from Holyrood. Tessa Ransford, the Poetry Library's director, had recently described the times we live in as 'an era of mass-trash' and maybe not just the library but the shift in Scotland's political fortunes marked a division between mass-trash and things of more lasting value. It is, at any rate, legitimate to hope so.

And there is another division, for me anyway; a watershed perhaps, or a borderline. Between that absence of consciousness of death, of the world, that was mine in 1963, when JFK was killed in Dallas, and my becoming a witness, in 1965, to Churchill's coffin rolling across the black-and-white TV screen on a gun carriage, something else happened to me. I moved from one country to another. Just the other week, thirty-six years after leaving, I went back to the old one. I stood in front of the house in Sevenoaks, Kent, where I spent the first five years of my life, and looked up at the windows of the bedroom in which I was born. The house was built in the 1930s. Externally, it hasn't changed at all. Internally, well, alterations are bound to have taken place after thirty-six years. There is a Native American proverb: everything changes, nothing changes.

The street itself looked the same to me: a cul-de-sac of identical, modestly sized detached houses, each with its garage, so that, as it had been in 1963, there was not a single car parked on the street. A street without cars looks very strange, in 1999. I used to ride my tricycle up and down it, imitating the cries of ragmen who came maybe twice a year with their horse and cart and who were as exotic as Roman charioteers. I recognised very little of the town itself, but the quiet street, its unpretentious houses, was the street of my memory. That was my five-year-old world, and it always will be.

You can't get much more English than Sevenoaks. Maybe it took me so long to go back because deep down I was afraid to think that, but for chance, I might have grown up as English as the town itself. That, and because for so long it seemed really to have nothing to do with me. Maybe it is my age, maybe the age of others, but this time, on a trip to London, that no longer seemed to be the case. I called on our next-door-but-one neighbours, still there after all those years, and we chatted about times so distant that I remember them not as a sequence but only as a handful of indistinct, unrelated incidents: my brother, in a seven-year-old's rage at some obscure injury done to his pride, punching his fist through a window-pane; snow one harsh winter that piled up taller than I was; the special way our neighbour made a boiled egg and toast, for when you were sick. 'You've got a Scottish accent,' she remarked, as if this was surprising. She and her husband were charming and kind. We had tea and Battenberg cake. They did not consider that they themselves had accents at all.

Chance, then. Or maybe not chance, but simply the way things happen: a job offer, better prospects, that kind of thing. I remember Dad opening an atlas, pointing with one finger and saying, 'We live here,' then moving the finger five hundred miles across the page and saying, 'How would you like to live here?' Unbridled excitement. Obviously that was where we were going. Our grandparents were Scots born and bred. We *felt* – we *were* – Scottish already. We would go on the sleeper, an adventure without precedent. We couldn't wait.

So I might have been English. According to my birth certificate, I suppose I am. Would I have been a different person? Undoubtedly, yes. Would the world have come to a stop? Of course not. You have to reach a place, from which you can look both far enough back and far enough forward, to realise that life is more complicated than that. Maybe, for me, that place was the fortnight in September, 1997, when Diana died and Scotland voted, finally and decisively, to have its parliament back. Life on either side of that vantage point seems more complete now, it makes more sense. In fiction, it's called resolution.

DILYS ROSE

Out of Touch: an extract from a work in progress

This is not the whole story but if I've done my job properly you won't be aware of my little excisions. I do try to cover my tracks, wherever possible. It does nobody any good – least of all me – to be able to detect my intervention. If you begin to suspect that I might have withheld something, remember that the mind's eye candy, the sticky floss whirling behind closed eyelids is almost always sweeter than the real thing. Besides, there's no such thing as the whole story.

Words:
I am finding words, names in particular, are becoming elusive, mutating creatures. I misread signs and wonder whether my vision is deteriorating. It is an occupational hazard. Long hours in a darkened room and so on. However, I can't shake off the notion that there is something else at work, some inner twist which turns one word into another. When I am writing my reports something different again happens. The most obvious linguistic tic is omission. Letters slip out of words, drop into limbo. Why? The brain impatiently racing ahead of the hand, the pen, the mouse? I have always written my reports slowly, meticulously. My attention

to such matters was one of the deciding factors in my being offered the post. That and my not entirely wholehearted support for self-rule. Yes, I believe in it, of course I do, in principle, in theory, in its ideal, utopian form but there are other considerations . . . what was I saying? Words, yes, words losing their letters . . .

I find myself re-reading newspaper headlines and, when I'm in the city, advertising slogans on buses and hoardings. Wordmongers, addicted to the process of double-think with which I'm all too familiar, continually bend and twist and reinvent the language. It will be interesting to see what becomes acceptable terminology in the extensively revised dictionary of the new nation. The word 'new' of course, is a nonsense in this context. No nation starts from scratch. When it comes to nations, there is no such thing as new, only the old with a face-lift and slathers of make-up to mask the ravages of history, geography, religion, economics and so on. Like a bygone star whose public appearances are limited by how long the pan-stick will stay in place and cover the surgeon's scars, this revived, renovated nation poses for the world's press holding a tense, slightly startled smile.

The Past:
The famously marketable refuge, strength and over-exploited treasure. The Heritage and Tourist Councils – to many these are peas in the same pod – are aggressively committed to developing the past. A national asset should be made to pay its way. As a result, it is now impossible to drive any distance at all without encountering a plaque indicating directions to some historical monument. More or less any old pile of stones

has been deemed a 'spot of interest'. What was once free and open countryside with no law of trespass is now littered with places which, if they don't merit an entrance fee, might still be called upon to contribute to the economy of the nearest village. Once a family saloon, a minibus or coach has grumbled up a bumpy rutted track so its passengers can view the remains of a Stone Age burial cairn or mediaeval fort, or sauntered from car parks to the turnpikes of the more recently official historical sights – obsolete colliery, shipping grave-yard, fisheries museum – a number of visitors will need to eat, drink or shop as well as avail themselves of the conveniently located facilities.

In the towns, an ordinary house happens to have been the childhood home of a person who grew up and became famous and so is awarded a plaque. Even if there is no actual building which is of interest in itself, there may still be some touristic angle: an otherwise nondescript crossroads could have been the starting point for some celebrated journey. The Albs have done more than their fair share of leaving home and sailing into the rose-tinted yonder, so why not slap on a plaque at each and every departure point?

City parks tend to benefit most from the long-established tradition of dedicating a bench seat to a respected citizen or personal friend. Surely these parks, by now, have ample seating. But what about the countryside? Think of the bench potential of some of those long country hikes people are so keen on. Clean, if not always dry places to put up one's blistered feet would surely be better than measly little mile-stones. Good quality wooden benches with metal or ceramic plaques for the dedications could be commissioned from local craftspeople. Individual hikers or rambling clubs would pay for and choose the design of a bench and specify the dedication. A job creation scheme which used local materials and employed local workers would not be reliant on government subsidy as it would pay for itself. It wouldn't make a profit but neither need it make a loss.

I can think of other uses for plaques. Particularly in the older cities, more or less any patch of pavement could, without straining the bounds of credibility, commemorate some noteworthy event. But what's to stop an imaginative tourist council inventing their own landmarks? Take a place which has nothing much to recommend it, make up a story, a route, employ and actor or two, a guide . . .

Maps:

Does going forward mean first of all going back? To drag oneself out of the past, to put one's feet firmly in the present and even consider dipping one's toes in the future, is it essential to deliberately, forcibly, tediously revisit that past, reassess it from the new independent point of view? It's worth remembering that the concept of forward into the future and back into the past is only a historical convention just as a north/south axis is a geographical convention which, incidentally, doesn't lend itself to some cartographic representations of the old or new Alba. As so much space is taken up by the sea, the country doesn't fit well into maps which are printed in the more broad than tall *landscape* format. For the same reason, Alba doesn't make good table mats. Only if the country is laid on its back and waving its ragged arms in the air, does the landscape layout work. *Portrait* format, more tall than broad, suits Alba better.

To create this nation, a smallish land mass with the silhouette of a hag, carline, crone, spaewife has been slashed through her cinched middle. Alba has retained the jutting chin and the humpback and, of course, the head, heart, breast, belly and amply-padded rump. Gladly, shamelessly, she cast off the trailing skirt with its frilly hem. The earliest maps of the nation were cruder and kinder, offering more homely, appealing contours – cuddly granny rather than hard-bitten hag but Alba, like my own homeland, was never a cuddly old dear.

My homeland, whose contours have changed more than once during my own lifetime, is contained in the *small packet* the postman responsibly delivered to me through the open window of his yellow van with red lions leaping over the bonnet. I haven't yet opened the recycled jiffy bag. That's because I know what it contains, you're thinking. I haven't opened my *small packet* because I don't want to be confronted by my own past, because I prefer to immerse myself in the past, present and possible future of this newly freed nation which must be better than what I've left behind. That packaged past of mine wouldn't, you're thinking, be worth mentioning if all it amounted to was a few snapshots of me and my sisters skating on the canal, sharing a meal or whatever. But that depends on one's point of view. There's some whatever, quite a bit of whatever but if I had to choose, it would be the skating snaps – again – I'd save from a burning building. And those in which my sisters and I are clinking our glasses in a toast. You have your famous skating minister, I have my infamous skating sisters.

Old names, old boundaries, old allegiances . . . On my

last stay in the capital I bought a couple of facsimiles of maps from the seventeenth and eighteenth centuries. Before and after, if you like. They are readily available in tourist shops but I bought mine from a studious but airy map centre where the assistant clearly preferred peering through a magnifying glass to operating the till. I like that. A salesperson's lack of enthusiasm for the till makes me want to buy more rather than less. I put the old maps on the walls of my bathroom with its ancient claw-footed bath.

Of the two I prefer the earlier one, the 'before', with its gentle, tentative contours and golden yellow border, giving the impression that the land was entirely fringed, like some tropical island, by sun-baked sand. In the seas, whiskered fishy monsters bigger than the bobbing sailing ships, raise their fantastic heads above painstakingly etched waves. The land itself is pocked all over with equilateral hillocks. Sea lochs wiggle in from the coast like tadpoles. The great ancient forest, a scrap of which surrounds my home, is suggested by stylised bluish trees. As they take up too much space, parts of the *Deucalidon, Irish* and *Germane* seas are given over to decorative inserts of the flag (inexplicably the wrong colour), the prancing heraldic lion and cameo illustrations of a low-land couple and their highland counterparts. The lowlanders are luxuriously dressed, the woman in ruff and head-dress, ermine cape and satin gown; the man in high hat, lace collar, cape and trews. Both are well shod. Apart from a wrap of plaid or herring-bone, the barefoot highlanders are naked.

The second map, produced shortly after the top half of the hag had been been stitched on to her skirt, had an altogether different purpose. Q: What in this land of mountains and forests, lochs and rivers was worth having? A: Fish. Was there enough? Where was it to be found? Would it be easier to harvest the plentiful supplies of cod and ling from the coast of *The North Part of Great Britain called Scotland*, as the *Kingdome of Scotland* had by then become, than to rely on more far-flung colonies like Nova Scotia? This is a more accurate map, more taut and angular, approaching the definitive hag shape, with handsome illustrations of the principal cities and fortifications of the time. It is undoubtedly a thoroughly researched and well-executed map but the cartographer's expansionist zeal sends shivers through me.

The contours of Alba's landmass are now long-established but the reshaping of the nation will continue to be in progress for years to come. The break from the south did not come about through a bloodbath, more of a slow drip, a gradual seeping, a filtering off of what are now considered inappropriate elements. Cleansing, as everybody knows, is now a proscribed word. And, of course, doesn't officially happen here. Recently, though, there have been some disturbing scenes at the border and I hear there are one or two difficult films on the subject coming my way on my next trip south. But that's work.

Wolves:

I find sawing logs therapeutic. A combination of strenuous outdoor effort and a visible sense of achievement, it is also a very effective way of warming up. Heat twice over. I am surrounded by a congregation of huge old pines, their branches bearded with lichen. Good air, if there's lichen about. Good, clean, Albish air. You savour your independent air. You also sell it to tourists in a silver can, embossed with a purple and green thistle motif: New Albish air. Uncontaminated by the imperialist filth on which the old hag choked for centuries. Yes, breathing is as much a pleasure here as a necessity, inhaling pine-scented air and listening to the sounds of the forest, distinct and discrete; a woodpecker doing some jazzy percussion in the treetops, plump lilac pigeons crooning throatily to each other and so on.

The other night, along with the now familiar sound of dead trees cracking and smashing to the forest floor, I heard the wolves. First a lone howl, then a duet, then the swelling ululation of the pack pealed round the hills, rippling over its own echoes, keening through the dark bowl of the valley. Some say that the sound of a pack howl makes their hair stand on end, others that it hits them in the solar plexus. I put on my dressing gown and slippers and went out into a mild, windless night. I followed the path through the trees towards the clearing, hurrying a little, half-hoping to see, by the light of a few stars and a sickle moon, an assembled pack, heads back, throats open.

Hated and feared by some for its predatory virtuosity and mesmeric yellow eyes, respected by others for its courage and family loyalties, the wolf has always been more than an animal. Of course, wolves haven't inhabited these forests for two hundred and fifty years. What I was hearing was the pack in the country park on the far side of the glen: imported wolves, wolves bred in captivity, wolves which have been given pet names by the park rangers, wolves which are contained inside double fences and may be observed closely and safely during their most intimate moments; as they crunch their lunchtime rabbits, as alpha male bullies his second in command, as the lower ranks skulk about, waiting their turn to eat, as the leaders mate, as the pack congregates on a rock as if to go hunting. Visitors click away at this or that demonstration of wolf behaviour. Some even volunteer to sponsor a wolf. Not only will they receive information and photos every so often but their names will also be inscribed on plaques which decorate the timber lookout towers. Another source of funding! Another use for plaques!

Some of the grand old pines under which I live – *grannies* as the Forest Development Council calls them – were probably around when wolves were still a free-ranging source of not altogether rational terror to the human population. These grannies would have been brash young saplings then, shooting up straight and slender, their own elders cracking and crashing around them, while hunters roamed the sunless forest floor with guns and hounds and the hope of payment. The price on a wolf's head was high and this was not just war waged against wolves, it was a deliberate extermination, an act of genocide. Elsewhere, the forest was torched to drive them out but here, harsh winters and keen huntsmen did the job. Once the last lonely wolf had been killed off, people had nothing to fear but each other.

A Memory:
Where I'm from, wolves still inhabit the forests and hills and the superstitious imaginations of country people. It was the end of a long, bitter winter. Easter was only a couple of weeks away and there was still snow on the ground. A wolf had got into a henhouse and through a mixture of hunger, fear and a

rush of adrenalin at tasting blood, had run amok, nipping and biting at random, terrifying the hens out of their fluttering wits. The farmer, a top-heavy man with hands like spades, had lumbered into the henhouse and shot the wolf.

That day our entire lunchtime conversation was taken up with the wolf shooting. My sisters, who'd witnessed the event, ate and blabbed away and were told off for talking with their mouths full. They interrupted each other's action replays of all the squawking and snarling, of feathers blowing through the door in clouds, of shots fired. Shortly after the sound of the shots – one sister said three, the other four – had faded away on the hot noon breeze, the farmer, whose name was Grass, emerged from the henhouse with the dripping wolf carcass slung over his shoulders like a fur stole. To spontaneous applause from adults and children alike, he crossed the yard and disappeared into his barn, leaving a red trail behind him. As there was nothing else to see at this point and because it was lunchtime, most of the audience drifted off, including my sisters, who were always hungry and keen to spread news. My appetite that day was dulled by my sisters' enthusiastic descriptions of the shoot-out in the henhouse but I was always a picky eater.

Immediately after lunch I was dragged, protesting, to the site of the morning's drama. It was all over now, there would be nothing to see, I whined in vain. By the time we reached the barn, a clutch of other children had already gulped down their lunch and regrouped at the scene of the action.

– He's been in there all the time.

– He didn't go for lunch.

– How d'you know if you were at home?

– I know. My dad said.

– How would your dad know if he was having his lunch? Has your dad got X-ray eyes?

– His dad's got cross eyes. And squint teeth.

– Hasn't!

– Has so. Crisscross eyes and teeth like a bag of clothes pegs.

A fight would have started there and then had Grass not kicked open the barn door and emerged. With a faint smile on his meaty face and a puffed-up air of importance, he strode across the yard, the wolfskin slung over an arm. We knew what was going to happen. We'd heard tell of the ritual, the charm against further calamity, the warning to other wolves to keep their distance. We'd heard tell of it but never seen it.

Grass hammered. We children hung back, whispering and giggling and nudging each other. When he had driven the final nail into the wolfskin, the farmer stepped back a few paces, paused briefly to inspect his handiwork, crossed the yard amidst our murmurs of awe and went inside for a late lunch. My sisters – and most of the other children – were beside themselves with excitement at being presented with the opportunity to inspect the wolfskin at close quarters, to stroke or tug the thick fur, to count the teeth and claws, to slip a finger or a whole hand between the gaping jaws. My memory of that day stops at the barn door, at the wolfskin spreadeagled on sun-bleached wood, a dark, heart-stopping star.

JAMES TRIMBLE

The Last Haircut
of the Twentieth Century

The glass door of the barbers' opened to let in a cold breeze and an unkempt youth. The cold air breathed life into the multitude of miniature wigs which lay strewn around the tiled floor. They slid across the surface in silence, their progress only halted by collisons with barbers' feet and the eventual closing of the door by a conscientious patron. Unkempt Youth sat down on the battered bench to await his turn. He could not be bothered to shut the door and regarded Conscientious Patron with a blank expression that you would not confuse with gratitude.

Unkempt Youth cast a rueful gaze at the four barber chairs. They were all occupied and the barbers danced and talked around their customers, showing equal dexterity with foot and mouth, clipping and snipping all the while. Unkempt Youth let his space-for-rent expression settle on one of the chairs and the person in it. The customer in question could not see Unkempt Youth's white ape goldfish combination face in the massive wall mirror in front of him. All he could see was his own reflection.

'Jist the usual,' said the customer. 'I'm doin' a big club the night.' The customer was an ace DJ, the best in Central

Scotland. This was self-professed and self-professed many times to anyone who could stand being in a room with him for more than five minutes. Ace Deejay was a 21st century sonic warrior on a mission to play his good time party hits to as many punters as possible. He spun his records (actually, he inserted compact discs) at weddings, eighteenths, twenty-firsts, birthdays in general, Christmas nights out, summer barbecues, boss or workmate leaving shindigs, anything that was going really. He would play at a funeral if so requested. What Ace Deejay liked more than anything, even playing his party hits, was to make money. Lots and lots of money.

'No' too short mind,' Ace Deejay said casually. The barber grunted an acknowledgement and went back to work on his customer's ginger head. Ace Deejay liked to look his best at all times. Unfortunately he had an unfeasibly large face and all the fancy blouses and novelty belt buckles he wore could not draw attention away from his huge orange visage. He had gained a massive amount of weight in the last two years. It seemed that the more the money rolled in the more the fat followed suit. Ace Deejay was surrounded by wads of cash and fat.

Ace Deejay had a plan. He knew exactly what he was doing with his life. Having left his dead-end, no-hope job at the cash-and-carry, he was ready to focus his full attention on building an empire. To this end, the one-time yes-man and crisp box mover had already managed to gather a small army of followers who would do his bidding. Most of them were ordinary lads with sufficiently less talent than Ace Deejay, allowing him to employ them without fear. These Lesser

Talents could be deployed around Central Scotland, doing the jobs their lesser talent was suited for. Ace Deejay did all the prestigious work, the big clubs and pubs, then handed the other end of the stick to his followers. When they received their twenty-five pounds at the end of a drunken, hostile night they did so with gratitude.

'Thanks Ace Deejay,' they would tell him, 'This'll supplement the poor wage my full-time, dead-end, no-hope job gives me.' Ace Deejay would smile and tell them he was glad to fork out the dosh. He would not tell them how glad he was that he was keeping more than seventy percent of the dosh the Lesser Talents made.

Ace Deejay's citrus fruit head swivelled around to admire what he thought to be one handsome devil looking back at him from the wall mirror. Things could only get better for Ace Deejay in the new millennium. He found himself struggling to hold the images of his future glory in his large head. Someone was distracting him. He could block out the redundant chatter of the barber and still keep a sense of all his success to come, but his mind was grounded at terminal one due to the ramblings of the customer in the next chair. The customer was having a lot of fuss smeared over him by both his attending barber and a young woman with bright purple hair. The customer's loud voice and outrageously baggy combat trousers led Ace Deejay to conclude that here was an attention seeker seeking attention.

'Aye, a mohican,' Attention Seeker enthused. 'Jist shave it aff it the sides n'leave the tope.' The barber looked down at the long mop of blond hair and then asked Attention Seeker's reflection, 'Are ye sure?'

'Aye.' Attention Seeker chuckled, happy at the attention he was getting. Bright Purple Hair was sitting on the battered bench behind him. She rolled her heavily made up eyes and went along with it, so deeply was she under his spell.

'He's in a band.' She explained to the barber in a voice so young and naive that it could only fail to induce vomiting in others of equal youth and naivety.

The band was a thrash metal outfit with punk pretensions and they were called Arse. Attention Seeker came up with that subtle name and he was the brains behind the band, as well as its lead singer and guitarist. The rest of the band were all still at school and worshipped Attention Seeker as if he was a new tube of spot cream. To them he was someone who had lived out their fantasies, someone who had been spat on by their favourite American musicians, someone who had even jammed with an extremely famous band's less famous support act's support act. Man he had done it all. At least that is what he led people to believe.

No one could work harder at trying to make something succeed than Attention Seeker. He placed advertisements in local newspapers informing journalists where Arse would be playing and when. For their part the journalists regarded him as terribly annoying and suspected that the band was actually named after him. The irritation and amusement he gave them came to a head when he phoned up one day, furious that his band's name had been misspelled.

'Well how d'you spell it?'

'A . . . R . . . S . . . E.'

'Hing on.' Rustle of paper. 'That's what we've pit.'

'Naw man.' Angry pause, 'It should be capital A small R, capital S, small E. The way ah wrote it oan the letter.'

Silence with a hint of giggle.

'Hello? Are ye still there?' Long pause.

'Aye, eh, still here. So are you spellin' it like that incase there's another band called Arse then?' Much laughter suppression.

'Eh?'

The irony was that for such a fun-loving extrovert Attention Seeker could not laugh at himself or even attempt to see the funny side of jokes aimed near or directly at him. Why, of course, he could laugh at a handicapped person struggle to count their change at a supermarket, but have that same handicapped person point at him and say 'Ah saw yer Arse last night it the pub.' the response would be a scowl at best or a short outburst of profanity at worst. He took himself too seriously. This was why he almost lost an ear when he turned to face the direction a bark of laughter had just come. Ace Deejay quickly looked back to his own reflection. The sight of Attention Seeker's head with one side shaved to a fine fuzz and one side long was just too much. He just had to let forth an indiscreet guffaw.

Ace Deejay glanced surreptitiously at Bright Purple Hair's reflection in the wall mirror. She reminded him of the sad cow he had been engaged to, only not so fat and with less acne. If there was one aspect of his meteoric rise to the small business elite that he regretted, it was getting involved with Sad Cow. She had to mess things up.

'Next?' the barber called as one of the four chairs became vacant. Ace Deejay watched the cautious approach of the next customer-for-the-chop and he smirked. With those glasses and clothes that called out 'I'm not with it!' and his head-bowed walk to the chair, the guy was obviously a social retard.

Social Retard took off his glasses and stared at his suddenly featureless reflection. His eyesight was so bad that his eyes needed those thick plastic lenses in front of them like a climber needs a strong rope and quality crampons.

'Eh, a gauge three at the back 'n'sides, an' jist cut the top short, ta, thanks.'

The barber took this into consideration and went to work. Social Retard had been listening to Attention Seeker talking about his band. He wanted to be in a band too. A few years ago he had even become immensely outgoing and phoned up someone who needed a guitarist. Social Retard was not an exceptional talent, but he could play a few tunes. This was thanks mainly to his having no pals, no girlfriend and no life. The scene was set for disappointment.

'So let's hear some of yer stuff.'

Social Retard plugged into his tiny amplifier and surveyed the strings of his cheap second-hand guitar. The three band members congregated in the rented practice room and tried not to laugh at the four-eyed figure of fun who was trying so hard to impress them.

'Ye kin turn it up if ye like', the band's drummer smirked. Social Retard had the amplifier up as high as it could go. He was giving them his best Claptonesque blues barrage and seemed unaware of the band members' amusement at the bluebottle in a tin cup sound coming from the miniscule amp. When he had finished his demonstration, Social Retard was asked to leave.

'Am no' wantin' to pit ye doon or nothin',' the lead singer drawled, reefer hanging from his lip, 'Bit naeb'dy wants t'hear that stuff anymore. Anybody can play that stuff man. We're tryin' t'sound original.'

Social Retard carried his tiny amp and cheap guitar back to the boot of his car and heard the metallic thunder rumble from the soundproof practice room three floors up. Social Retard had to admit, they did sound pretty original.

'Nice job man.'

Attention Seeker admired his new look in the mirror. Bright Purple Hair was so delighted that the stud in her tongue almost popped out.

'It's brilliant!' she said reverentially.

'I'll just tidy it up a wee bit,' the barber chirped up, just in case Attention Seeker and Bright Purple Hair were about to share a passionate moment in the barber's chair. The new look would confirm Attention Seeker as the ultimate rebel at his workplace. Apart from being in Arse, he was also an administrative officer with a prominent government agency in Falkirk. Amazingly, for all his weird attire and non-conformity, he had already been promoted twice in under three years. His workmates were beginning to find him tiresome. It was not just the posturing and the tall tales, he had started to become downright obnoxious. Some speculated that it was down to the lack of success he was having with Arse, while others suspected that he was a sociopath in denial and had recently seen the light.

A young lad who would go to lunch and teabreaks with him bore the brunt of Attention Seeker's fury when he was not getting people's full attention. If conversations strayed from the subjects that were close to Attention Seeker's heart (music, UFOs, Bright Purple Hair, food, anything about him) he would start drumming on the table. If this did not get any attention he would drum his fingers louder, he would belch in people's faces, he would spill the contents of cups or soft drink cans onto laps and if these tactics failed he would withdraw and start to mumble his latest song into the ether. If it was a bad move to ignore Attention Seeker, it was positively deadly to acknowledge him. As Young Lad discovered.

'How come yer band's called Arse?'

Attention Seeker turned slowly and regarded Young Lad with a look of complete indifference. He was actually quite pleased that the conversation had come back round to him again, but he was not about to show it, especially to Young Lad.

'How come you're a skinny wee get?' he growled and looked around the table to see if others found his retort as amusing as he did.

'I wis jist askin''—'

'Aye, well don't.'

This was the enigma of Attention Seeker. He would go to extraordinary lengths to attract attention and when it was heaped upon him he pretended to take offense at the most inoffensive questions.

*

The night passed into early morning and Ace Deejay started putting his top party tunes into their case. It had been a lacklustre crowd (the bouncer applied pressure on Ace Deejay to 'F***in' play somethin' decent!' due to lack of bodies boogying) and he just wanted to collect his fee and split.

'Awright?'

Ace Deejay looked up and laid his peepers on a young girl of immense girth. Her face looked like it had been used as a dartboard, so many blemishes and sores adorned it. The girl had been jiggling her plumpness near Ace Deejay's decks all night.

'I really enjoyed yer music.'

'Cheers.'

That was how Ace Deejay met Sad Cow. She became his property after that and the two of them were never seen more than ten feet away from each other for the next four months. Sad Cow would accompany him to his gigs and he taught her the finer points of inserting compact discs and lifting sound and lighting equipment. In a few weeks she became so good at it that he let her lift the sound and lighting equipment by herself, while he inserted the compact discs.

Social Retard was a hopeless romantic, a tragic character flaw for someone with no confidence. He would try to let his feelings flow out through writing. He wrote his first and last novel at the age of seventeen, using the word-processor in the Stirling District Council Transport Department, where he was marooned as a youth trainee. Social Retard's only claim to fame was that he was the only youth trainee in Central

Scotland to hand in a letter of resignation. It was duly pointed out to him that he did not actually have a job to resign from.

The romance was knocked out of him when he entered his first real job. Social Retard had never had a girlfriend of any sort in the first twenty years of his life. To say he was inexperienced would be a slight on inexperienced people.

He met her on the first day of his new job. They had to introduce each other to the assembled throng and he found out a lot about her. Social Retard found out she was quite an independent lady and although she was the same age as him, seemed much older. He also found out that she was diabetic but did not let it get her down. Independent Lady did not find out much about Social Retard. There was little to find out. He had yet to take up the guitar at this point, had no friends, lived with his parents and possessed even less confidence than when he was a teenager. He did have a car however.

A phone rang. It was a mobile phone and it rang to the tune of 'Popeye the Sailor'. It was attached to Ace Deejay's belt. Thankfully, the barber had finished working on his customer's massive noggin and was able to attend to the cash register as Ace Deejay took the call.

'Aye, what is it, am gettin' ma haircut.'

The expression on Ace Deejay's face changed from annoyance to elation in the blink of an eye.

'Brilliant! That's great.'

Attention Seeker watched this unfold as the barber shaved off the surviving hairs from each side of his scalp. He made a mental note to purchase a mobile phone.

*

After going to lunch together for several months at their work, Social Retard and Independent Lady built up a strange relationship. It was strange because Independent Lady did not actually like Social Retard very much. She tolerated him because he gave her lifts home to her small flat. She was also quite lonely, having moved to the area from far off, leaving her friends and ex-boyfriend behind and Social Retard was better than nothing until something better arrived. She was already making new friends, but could not break away from her tie with Social Retard. It all came to a head when he asked her if she wanted to go out one night. Against her better judgement she agreed. After all it had been a long time since anyone had shown such an obvious interest in her and Social Retard was a man, albeit a weak, spineless one.

'How much do I owe ye?' Ace Deejay asked the barber, who answered him and waited for his money. Ace Deejay produced an enormous wad of cash from his pocket and handed the barber a tenner. The barber rang it up on the register and handed Ace Deejay back his change. If the barber was hoping a tip was forthcoming from his affluent customer he was to be disappointed.

'Here,' Ace Deejay said as he handed something to the barber. 'Thank's fir the trim.'

The barber looked down at the business card he had just received.

'Anytime ye need a disco fir a party, give's a call.' And with that, Ace Deejay left the barber shop. Unkempt Youth had already moved into the vacant chair.

*

Ace Deejay was overjoyed. The telephone call had just confirmed that he had landed a residency at an upmarket club in Edinburgh. If things worked out he would be handling the Hogmanay night disco and take his party hits into a new century while his adoring public danced until dawn and he raked in the hard cash. Even the presence of Sad Cow somewhere in the back of his mind could not dampen his enthusiasm for the future. A new era for Scotland and a new era for Ace Deejay. Sad Cow could moan for her child support all she wanted. To tell you the truth Ace Deejay never really liked her anyway and even less so when she got herself up the duff. He had brief ideas of raising an heir to his empire, but soon tired of the responsibility. He stayed just long enough for the thing to be born, then he left. She was dragging him down, so he cut her loose.

Attention Seeker smiled at Unkempt Youth, who just stared at him vacantly with his damp pastry face.

'You look magic!' Bright Purple Hair gushed as Attention Seeker rose majestically from the chair. As he settled up with the barber, he began to think that the next century was when Arse would finally make it big. Some cueball-headed record mogul would drop into the pub for a swift half and hear them play. They would be signed up before he had finished his drink.

The closest Attention Seeker had come to some kind of fame was on the television programme 'Freaky but Fact' having claimed to have seen and photographed an unidentified flying object. The only bad thing that came out of his television appearance was that he had been forbidden from mentioning Arse. Despite missing out on a plug for his band, he was happy about the attention he gained. It could have gone much worse. If the programmes researchers had been willing to look deeper and ignore the Bonnybridge UFO frenzy for one moment, they would have uncovered Attention Seeker's most elaborate ploy yet in his bid for fame. His father was a photographer and Attention Seeker had studied photography at college. This is not evidence that the photograph had been faked, but the journalists who had been annoyed and amused by Attention Seeker could have told the researchers something.

The photograph of the glowing sphere in the night sky was just the latest in a long line of hoaxes perpetrated by Attention Seeker. He had been sending fake photographs into the local newspapers for over a year. One journalist told his colleagues how he witnessed Attention Seeker and an accomplice (the drummer from Arse) throwing a traffic sign into the air and photographing it.

Unkempt Youth began to panic, although no one would realise it. His outward appearance was fixed from the time he collapsed out of bed in the afternoon, until he dragged his lanky carcass back into it when the birds began to tweet. A zombie was more animated than Unkempt Youth and it would be a toss-up as to who you would get the best conversation from. All the same, he was worried. He had not felt this way since last week when he met this guy outside a pub.

The next century was going to bring more of the same for Social Retard. It had been a quiet Christmas and it was going to be a quiet new year. He would probably sit in his bedroom in his parents' house, plonking away on his guitar and watching people having a much better time than him on the television.

'Have a drink.'

Social Retard looked down at his clasped hands.

'I'd better no',' he said. 'I'm drivin'—'

Independent Lady shrugged and sat down next to him on the sofa. She had just experienced an embarrassing night out with Social Retard. Her idea of going out for dinner involved three courses, candles and coffee. A burger and fries while sitting next to a kiddie's playpen almost made her laugh in Social Retard's face and walk away. Instead, they went back to her small flat. Maybe she could arouse something hidden deep within Social Retard that would surprise them both.

Two hours into the two of them sitting together on the sofa the only thing Independent Lady had discovered was that Social Retard was either gay or exceedingly dim. She had done everything she could to let him know that he could lay some moves on her. She kept throwing her head back and resting it on the back of the sofa, looking at him from the corners of her eyes. When Social Retard was looking through the photographs she had given him and admired a particular dress she had on at a party, she told him she had it in her wardrobe.

'I could put it on if you like.' she purred. Social Retard acted like he never heard and focused even more attention on the photographs in front of him.

The end came swiftly. Social Retard had his coat on and almost ran out of the door.

'Hang on a minute.' she called after him and walked up the hallway towards him. 'Thank's for taking me out tonight.' She embraced him as seductively as she could. His heavy coat was a bit of a handicap however.

'Eh, right. Well, I'll see ye at work.'

The barber finally came over and stood behind Unkempt Youth.

'What's it to be today then?' he enquired. Unkempt Youth looked at his long face in the mirror and the greasy black hair hanging limply in his eyes and against his cheek.

Social Retard was in love. He could not stop thinking about Independent Lady. He asked her out again and vowed to himself that he was going to do a better job of it this time. He even bought her a massive stuffed toy she had admired. He was ready to tell her how he felt about her. Then the phone rang. Independent Lady could not go out with him; family business had cropped up. Social Retard was not crushed, there would be another time.

There was not another time for Social Retard and Independent Lady. Her ex-boyfriend had turned up and wanted to remove the ex from his official title. She removed it and broke the news to Social Retard at work. It was like a kick in the groin, except the pain lasted most of the day and most of the rest of that week. They still went to lunch together, but Social Retard was so ill-equipped to deal with the rejection that he did not talk to her at all. She soon plucked up the courage to stop going to lunch with him and began going with other friends. Social Retard had no other friends. He just kept his head down and went about his mediocre life. The stuffed toy ended up with his mother.

Unkempt Youth could not remember what he and This Guy had been arguing about that night outside the pub. He could not remember if he stuck the knife in This Guy's neck or his stomach. He did remember that This Guy did not get up again and he also remembered that the police were looking for a thin man with long dark hair.

'What's it to be today then?'

Unkempt Youth looked at his long face in the mirror and the greasy black hair hanging limply in his eyes and against his cheek.

'Shave it inti the wid.'

The Contributors

TONI DAVIDSON was born in Ayr in 1965. He has edited the anthologies *And Thus I Will Freely Sing* (Polygon) and *Intoxication* (Serpent's Tail). His first novel, *Scar Culture*, was published by Rebel Inc in July 1999 and has been translated into several languages. He is currently working on his second novel, *Wild Justice*.

CHRIS DOLAN was born in Glasgow and has lived in Spain and Portugal. He has studied at both Glasgow and Lisbon universities and was the Scottish Director of CSU before writing full-time. He still works as a consultant for UNESCO. He writes for page, stage and screen.

ANNE DONOVAN lives in Glasgow. Over the past three years her stories have appeared in anthologies and literary magazines and been broadcast on Radio Scotland. In 1997 she won the *Scotland on Sunday/Macallan* short story competition.

PETER DORWARD was born in St Andrews in 1963. He has worked as a hop picker, barman, driver, aid-worker, viola player and soap opera script advisor. He is currently a part-time General Practitioner in London.

DAVID EDWARDS was born in Leicester in 1965 and moved to Edinburgh at the age of seven. He studied at Glasgow University and currently lives and works in Edinburgh.

DAVID EWEN was born in Aberdeen. He studied engineering at university and now works as a journalist with the *Evening Express* in his home town. He has also scripted *Norman Love: Burglar*, voted Best Short at the Edinburgh Fringe Film and Video Festival.

FIONA GIBSON has worked for various youth magazines including *Jackie, Just 17, Bliss and More!* For the past three years she has freelanced for various publications as well as having her own monthly column in the women's glossy magazine *Red*. She has twin sons – two-year-olds Sam and Dexter. 'Sugar Baby' is her first published work of fiction.

KATE GRAHAM was born in Bridge of Allan and bred in Perthshire. She now divides her time between Perthshire and Edinburgh, where she is employed as a civil servant.

STEPHEN LIVINGSTON was born in 1971. He graduated from Glasgow University in 1999. 'Choose Your Future' is his first piece of published fiction.

ALEX MAHON was born in Denistoun, Glasgow, and has spent most of his adult life abroad. He currently works in a Call Centre in Glasgow. 'Rocking the Chocolate Machine' is his first published work.

BRIAN MCCABE is one of Scotland's most acclaimed contemporary poets. His collections include *Spring's Witch, One Atom to Another* and *Body Parts*. He has also published two collections of short stories; *The Lipstick Circus* and *In a Dark Room with a Stranger*, and a novel, *The Other McCoy*. He lives in Edinburgh with his family.

IAN MITCHELL was born in Ayr in 1935. Until taking early retirement in 1985 he taught Modern Languages at Jordanhill College. Now a translator from German, he has also written two books on Scotland – one in German and one in English. He is married with two sons.

WILLIAM MUIR was born in Glasgow and lives in Edinburgh. He is currently working on a novel *The 18th Pale Descendant*, about a sinister form of National Lottery in a futuristic Britain. 'The Second Coming' is his first piece of published fiction.

JANET PAISLEY is an award winning poet, writer and playwright. Her collections include *Reading the Bones, Alien Crop* (both poetry), and *Wild Fire* (stories). Her plays include *Refuge* and *Winding String*. Internationally anthologised, her work is also broadcast and taught in schools. The single parent of six sons, she lives in a small village near Falkirk.

JAMES ROBERTSON was born in 1958. He has published two collections of short stories; *Close* and *The Ragged Man's Complaint*; two collections of poetry, *Sound-Shadow* and *I Dream of Alfred Hitchcock*; and a book of *Scottish Ghost Stories*. His first novel, to be published in 2000, is *The Fanatic*. He lives in Fife.

DILYS ROSE has published two collections of poems, three of short stories, most recently *War Dolls*, and a novel, *Pest Maiden*. She has received several awards for her writing and is currently working on a second novel and, as always, more stories. She lives in Edinburgh.

JAMES TRIMBLE was born in 1974. By day he works as a civil servant in Falkirk, while at night he is completing a degree in Film and Media/English at Stirling University. 'The Last Haircut of the Twentieth Century' is his first published work.